Date Due

BRO DART   CAT. NO. 23 233   PRINTED IN U.S.A.

NOMOGRAPHY

NOMOGRAPHY

L. IVAN EPSTEIN

Lowell Technological Institute, Lowell, Massachusetts

M·D·K

INTERSCIENCE PUBLISHERS, INC., NEW YORK
INTERSCIENCE PUBLISHERS LTD., LONDON

INTERSCIENCE PUBLISHERS, INC.

250 Fifth Avenue, New York 1, N. Y.

For Great Britain and Northern Ireland:

INTERSCIENCE PUBLISHERS LTD.

88/90 Chancery Lane, London W. C. 2

PRINTED IN THE UNITED STATES OF AMERICA
BY MACK PRINTING COMPANY, EASTON, PA.

TO
MY FORMER PROFESSORS
at the
CALIFORNIA INSTITUTE
OF TECHNOLOGY

PREFACE

Although a number of books are already available which discuss methods for the construction of nomograms, a need exists for a book that combines the discussion and methods of construction with a thorough presentation of the underlying theory. The present volume is intended to fulfill this need. Some of the subject matter included, notably Section 7.5, has not been presented in book form before.

Chapters I, II, III, V, and VI together form an elementary text. Here, the presentation is of necessity more detailed than in the remaining chapters. The omission of Chapter IV will not cause a loss of continuity. Only in Chapters VII and VIII is a knowledge of differential and integral calculus expected of the reader. Otherwise, only a knowledge of the elements of analytical geometry is required. The reader may acquire the necessary knowledge of determinants, matrices, and the rudiments of projective geometry from the present text. An attempt has been made to make the presentation mathematically rigorous insofar as this could be done on a relatively elementary level. A few theorems taken from projective geometry have been stated without proof, but they are not altogether necessary for an understanding of the subject matter. In the last chapter, two propositions are stated without proof because the proofs would have been far too long and advanced for inclusion. The qualified reader must be referred to the original paper quoted in the bibliography for the proofs. Here, also, the theorems are not necessary for an understanding of the subsequent subject matter.

Only a few problems have been included. In part, these allow the student to supply some of the simpler proofs or to discover additional subject matter for himself. The inclusion of long lists of practice problems was not considered desirable since the need for them has been adequately met by other books.

It is a pleasure to thank those colleagues in Baltimore who have made helpful suggestions. I am indebted to Mr. T. Woodard for arousing my interest in the subject; to Mr. M. L. Coon, Jr., for reading portions of the manuscript, offering constructive criticism, and drawing the subject matter of Section 6.1 and Chapter VIII to my attention; and to the publisher's consultant, Professor John Happel of New York University, for drawing the subject matter of Section 6.2 to my attention.

L. Ivan Epstein

CONTENTS

CHAPTER I

Determinants

CHAPTER II

Nomograms

CHAPTER III

Projective Transformations

CHAPTER IV

Matrix Multiplication

CHAPTER V

More Than Three Variables

CHAPTER VI

Empirical Nomography

CHAPTER VII

Kellogg's Method

CHAPTER VIII

Nonprojective Transformations

CHAPTER I

Determinants

1.1. Definition

A matrix is defined to be a rectangular array of numbers, consisting of columns and rows, such that one number is written at the intersection of any one column with any one row. The individual numbers are called the elements of the matrix. One widely used notation for a matrix is

$$\begin{bmatrix} a_{11} & a_{12} & a_{13}\ldots\ldots a_{1j}\ldots\ldots a_{1n} \\ a_{21} & a_{22} & a_{23}\ldots\ldots a_{2j}\ldots\ldots a_{2n} \\ \ldots\ldots\ldots\ldots\ldots\ldots\ldots\ldots\ldots\ldots \\ a_{i1} & a_{i2} & a_{i3}\ldots\ldots a_{ij}\ldots\ldots a_{in} \\ \ldots\ldots\ldots\ldots\ldots\ldots\ldots\ldots\ldots\ldots \\ a_{m1} & a_{m2} & a_{m3}\ldots\ldots a_{mj}\ldots\ldots a_{mn} \end{bmatrix},$$

where the first subscript denotes the row number and the second subscript, the column number. Where no confusion can arise, we may use the notation $[a_{ij}]$ or $[a]$ for short. Instead of the square brackets which we have placed around the matrix, some authors use parentheses or double vertical lines. Some authors use a superscript in place of one of the two subscripts.

To round out the definition of a matrix, we should define the concepts of addition and multiplication of matrices. However, we shall postpone these subjects until Chapter IV.

If the matrix has as many rows as columns, it is said to be a square matrix. Let n be the number of rows (or columns) of a square matrix, and let us form a product of n elements of the

1

matrix such that no two elements are from the same row or the same column. The values of the first subscript of the elements in such a product must be all the integers from 1 through n. The same is true of the second subscript. Let the elements be arranged in the order of increasing value of the first subscript. We say that there is an inversion of the second subscript whenever a second subscript precedes one of smaller value. For instance, in the product $a_{14} a_{22} a_{35} a_{43} a_{56} a_{61}$, where the first subscripts increase from left to right, the second subscripts are 4, 2, 5, 3, 6, 1. Now, we say that there is an inversion among these subscripts whenever a greater number precedes a smaller one. In the present example, there are seven inversions, to wit: 4 precedes 2, 3, and 1 (three inversions); 2 precedes 1 (a fourth inversion); 5 precedes 3 and 1 (another two inversions); 6 precedes 1 (the last and seventh). Now let us form all possible products of n matrix elements such that no two elements are taken from the same row or the same column. Let us add those containing an even number of inversions and subtract those containing an odd number of inversions. The result is called the determinant of the square matrix. It is denoted by the same symbol as the matrix from which it was obtained, except that the square brackets are replaced with thin vertical lines thus:

$$
\begin{vmatrix}
a_{11} & a_{12} & a_{13}\ldots\ldots a_{1j}\ldots\ldots a_{1n} \\
a_{21} & a_{22} & a_{23}\ldots\ldots a_{2j}\ldots\ldots a_{2n} \\
\cdots\cdots\cdots\cdots\cdots\cdots\cdots\cdots\cdots\cdots \\
a_{i1} & a_{i2} & a_{i3}\ldots\ldots a_{ij}\ldots\ldots a_{in} \\
\cdots\cdots\cdots\cdots\cdots\cdots\cdots\cdots\cdots\cdots \\
\cdots\cdots\cdots\cdots\cdots\cdots\cdots\cdots\cdots\cdots \\
a_{n1} & a_{n2} & a_{n3}\ldots\ldots a_{nj}\ldots\ldots a_{nn}
\end{vmatrix}
$$

or $|a_{ij}|$ or $|a|$ for short. Note the distinction between a determinant and a matrix: A matrix is a rectangular array of numbers and cannot be described by a single numerical value. A determinant is a single number, which is a function of the elements of the matrix. If the matrix has n rows and n columns, its determinant is said to be of the nth order. It is perfectly well possible for two matrices, even with unequal n, to have the same determinant. Strictly speaking, it is wrong to speak of the elements, rows, and columns of a determinant. More precisely, we should speak of the elements, rows, and columns of the matrix whose determinant is under discussion. Nonetheless, the first form of expression is widely used where no confusion can arise.

1.2. Second- and Third-Order Determinants

The expression for a determinant in terms of the elements of a square matrix is called the expansion of the determinant. From the definition of a determinant, the expansion of a second-order determinant is obtained:

$$\begin{vmatrix} a_{11} & a_{12} \\ a_{21} & a_{22} \end{vmatrix} = +a_{11}a_{22} - a_{12}a_{21}. \tag{1.1}$$

Here, there are only two possible ways of forming a product of two elements which are not from the same row or the same column, hence only two terms in the expansion. We have arranged the elements in each term in the order of increasing value of the first subscript, as required for application of the definition of "inversion." In the first term, the second subscripts are in increasing order, therefore there is no inversion, and this term is preceded by a plus sign. In the second term, the second subscripts are in the order 2, 1. Hence, there is one inversion, and the second term is preceded by a minus sign. The expansion is easily memorized with the aid of the following rule: the elements on each diagonal are multiplied together. If the diagonal slopes down from left to right, a plus sign is written in front of the product. If the diagonal slopes up from left to right, a minus sign is written in front of the product. ("Going uphill is hard work. That makes it minus.") The (algebraic) sum of the products with signs as described is the value of the determinant.

THEOREM 1.1. The value of a third-order determinant is given by

$$\begin{vmatrix} a_{11} & a_{12} & a_{13} \\ a_{21} & a_{22} & a_{23} \\ a_{31} & a_{32} & a_{33} \end{vmatrix} = a_{11}\,a_{22}\,a_{33} + a_{12}\,a_{23}\,a_{31} + a_{13}\,a_{21}\,a_{32} \\ - a_{13}\,a_{22}\,a_{31} - a_{11}\,a_{23}\,a_{32} - a_{12}\,a_{21}\,a_{33}. \quad (1.2)$$

This may be verified from the definition of a determinant. Given that the first indices of the three factors in each term are the numbers 1, 2, 3, the second indices must be the same numbers arranged in all possible orders. It is known from the theory of permutations that 3! such arrangements are possible. Hence the 3rd-order determinant has 3! or six terms in its expansion. (In general, an nth-order determinant has $n!$ terms in its expansion.) As for the signs, one more example should suffice. In the term $a_{12}\,a_{23}\,a_{31}$, the second subscripts are in the order 2, 3, 1. Here, 2 precedes 1, and 3 precedes 1. The number of inversions is two, which is even. Hence, the term is to be added.

PROBLEM 1.1. The reader should verify the signs of the other terms as an exercise.

The expansion of a third-order determinant may also be obtained by a simple rule-of-thumb. The first two columns

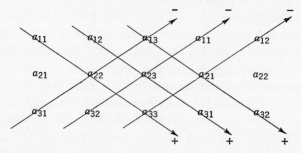

are rewritten in order after the third. Then form the six diagonal products as shown. Again, those taken in the downhill direction from left to right are written with a plus sign, those taken in the uphill direction, with a minus sign. The resulting terms are then added. With a little practice, the reader will learn to visualize this pattern without rewriting the first two columns. This rule of expansion is an obvious extension of the rule for second-order determinants. It is, however, not valid for determinants of order higher than the third.

PROBLEM 1.2. Expand the standard fourth-order determinant.

PROBLEM 1.3. In Section 1.1, we said that two square matrices with unequal number of columns may have equal determinants. Construct a numerical example to illustrate this. Let one matrix have two rows and two columns, the other, three.

Hint: Choose all matrix elements except the last one arbitrarily. Then adjust the last one to make the two determinants equal.

1.3. Some Fundamental Theorems

We go on to demonstrate some fundamental theorems which we shall need in later chapters.

THEOREM 1.2. If two rows (columns) of a determinant are interchanged, the determinant changes sign.

We shall demonstrate the proposition only for an interchange of two rows. The proof for an interchange of two columns is similar. We shall first demonstrate the proposition for the special case where two adjacent rows are interchanged. We suppose the new determinant expanded. Each term in the expansion of the new determinant could have been obtained from one of the terms in the expansion of the old determinant by an interchange of two neighboring factors. Let the kth and the $(k + 1)$th rows be interchanged. If we write $b_{ij} = a_{ij}$ when $i \neq k$ and $i \neq k + 1$, and if we write $b_{kj} = a_{k+1,j}$ and $b_{k+1,j} = a_{kj}$, then in every term in the expansion expressed in terms of the b's, the first subscripts will once again be in increasing order from left to right. As for the second subscripts, the number of their inversions will have been changed (that is increased in some cases and decreased in the others) by one.

In other words, if the number of such inversions was formerly even, it becomes odd, and *vice versa*. In either case, the term changes sign. Since every term in the expansion changes sign, the determinant as a whole changes sign.

To prove the proposition in general, consider the case where the two rows to be interchanged are separated by m intervening rows. Let the two rows to be interchanged be denoted by A and B. The operation of interchanging A and B may be broken down into a number of steps as follows: A is successively interchanged with the m intervening rows, so that it becomes B's nearest neighbor. A and B are interchanged. B is successively interchanged with the m rows which formerly intervened between A and B. This accomplishes the desired interchange of A and B while restoring the other rows to their former places. A total of $2m + 1$ interchanges of adjacent rows were necessary in all. These cause the determinant to change sign $2m + 1$ times. This is an odd integral number of changes of sign when m is any integer and amounts to a single change of sign. This proves the proposition.

PROBLEM 1.4. Prove the proposition for an interchange of two columns.

From Theorem 1.2 we prove the following theorem as a corollary.

THEOREM 1.3. If two or more rows (columns) of a determinant are identical, the determinant vanishes.

Proof: From Theorem 1.2, we know that an interchange of two identical columns or rows changes the sign of the determinant. However, since the two columns (or rows) are identical, their interchange should have no effect. These two statements can both be true only if the determinant vanishes.

THEOREM 1.4. If, in a determinant, the columns and rows are interchanged (so that columns become rows and rows become columns), the determinant remains unchanged. In symbols

$$|a_{ij}| = |a_{ji}|.$$

We may say that the determinant has been reflected in its principal diagonal (that diagonal which runs from the upper left to the lower right).

Proof: By interchanging rows with columns, we interchange the two subscripts of every element. Now, the expansion of an nth-order determinant contains all possible terms which are products of n elements such that no two elements are taken from the same row or the same column. The same must be true of the determinant obtained by interchanging rows with columns. The only conceivable change is that some of the terms may have changed sign. It remains to be proved that this is not the case. In other words, we must prove that if we interchange the two subscripts of every element, the sign to be written in front of any term of the expansion will not change. This may be demonstrated as follows. If, before the interchange of rows with columns, the first subscripts were in order of increasing value, then, after the interchange, the second subscripts will be in order. We may restore the usual order of the first subscript by rearranging the elements in the term. This rearrangement has the effect of introducing an inversion of second subscripts wherever an inversion of first subscripts existed before. Hence, whatever the number of inversions of the second subscript in any term of the original determinant, the corresponding term formed by interchange of rows with columns has the same number of inversions of the second subscript written in the customary form and is therefore to be preceded by the same sign. This proves the proposition.

We proved Theorem 1.2 only for two rows. With the aid of Theorem 1.4, the corresponding theorem for columns now becomes a mere corollary of the former. Likewise, Theorems 1.5, 1.6, 1.7, and Eqs. (1.3) and (1.4) below need be proved only for rows *or* columns. In each case, the other theorem follows with the aid of Theorem 1.4.

THEOREM 1.5. If all elements in one column (or row) of a determinant are multiplied (or divided) by the same factor, the determinant is multiplied (or divided) by the factor.

Proof: Every term in the expansion of the determinant contains one and only one element from each row and from each column. If all the elements in one column are multiplied by the same factor, each term in the expansion contains exactly one element from that column and is therefore multiplied by that factor. Hence the determinant is multiplied by that factor.

THEOREM 1.6. If each element of one column (or row) is written as a sum of two terms, the determinant can be written as a sum of two determinants, thus:

$$\begin{vmatrix} a_{11} + b_{11} & a_{12} & a_{13} \\ a_{21} + b_{21} & a_{22} & a_{23} \\ a_{31} + b_{31} & a_{32} & a_{33} \end{vmatrix} = \begin{vmatrix} a_{11} & a_{12} & a_{13} \\ a_{21} & a_{22} & a_{23} \\ a_{31} & a_{32} & a_{33} \end{vmatrix} + \begin{vmatrix} b_{11} & a_{12} & a_{13} \\ b_{21} & a_{22} & a_{23} \\ b_{31} & a_{32} & a_{33} \end{vmatrix}.$$

Proof: Every term in the expansion of the given determinant can be written as a sum of two terms by the distributive law. For instance

$$(a_{11} + b_{11})a_{22} a_{33} = a_{11} a_{22} a_{33} + b_{11} a_{22} a_{33}.$$

The resulting terms, when properly grouped together, form the expansions of two determinants.

THEOREM 1.7. If one column (or row) or multiple thereof is added to another column (or row) of the same determinant, the value of the determinant does not change. For instance

$$\begin{vmatrix} a_{11} & a_{12} & ka_{12} + a_{13} \\ a_{21} & a_{22} & ka_{22} + a_{23} \\ a_{31} & a_{32} & ka_{32} + a_{33} \end{vmatrix} = \begin{vmatrix} a_{11} & a_{12} & a_{13} \\ a_{21} & a_{22} & a_{23} \\ a_{31} & a_{32} & a_{33} \end{vmatrix}.$$

This theorem is a corollary of Theorems 1.3, 1.5, and 1.6.

PROBLEM 1.5. The proof is left as an exercise for the reader.

1.4. Minors and Cofactors

Let the rth row and the sth column be deleted from a determinant $|a_{ij}|$. The resulting determinant is called the *minor* of the element and will be denoted here by A_{rs}. More precisely, it is called a first minor of the given determinant. More generally, the result of deleting m columns and m rows is called an mth minor.

In the expansion of a determinant, we may gather together all terms containing a given element a_{rs} and write these terms collectively as the product of a_{rs} by a coefficient B_{rs} which we shall determine presently. This coefficient is called the *cofactor* of the element a_{rs}. Since no term in the expansion may contain two elements from the same row (or column), we may write the determinant in the form

$$|a_{ij}| = a_{r1}B_{r1} + a_{r2}B_{r2} + a_{r3}B_{r3} + \ldots + a_{rs}B_{rs} + \ldots$$
$$+ a_{rn}B_{rn}. \quad (1.3)$$

In general, we shall use the notation

$$\sum_{i=p}^{q} C_i$$

to denote the series $C_p + C_{p+1} + C_{p+2} + C_{p+3} + \ldots + C_q$, that is the sum of all terms of the form C_i, where i takes on all integral values from p through q. With this notation, we may write Eq. (1.3):

$$|a_{ij}| = \sum_{s=1}^{n} a_{rs}B_{rs}. \quad (1.4)$$

We shall now prove that $B_{11} = A_{11}$. Setting $r = 1$ in Eq. (1.4), we obtain all those terms containing a_{11} by starting with the term $a_{11}a_{22}a_{33}\ldots a_{nn}$ and permuting the second subscripts of all factors except the first in all possible ways, assigning signs as usual. Now the second subscript of the first factor a_{11} cannot possibly contribute to the number of inversions, since all succeeding second subscripts are greater than 1. Hence, the cofactor of the element a_{11} is identical with the minor.

To obtain an expression for the cofactor of the element a_{rs}, we make use of Theorem 1.2. If the rth row (or the sth column) is interchanged with either of its nearest neighbors, the minor of the element a_{rs} remains unchanged. (This would not be the case if the two rows or columns interchanged were not nearest neighbors.) Now we can move the element a_{rs} to the first row by interchanging the row in which it occurs $r - 1$ times with its nearest neighbor above. We can then move a_{rs} to the first column, that is, to the position formerly occupied by a_{11}, by interchanging the column in which it occurs $s - 1$ times in succession with its nearest neighbor on the left. When these interchanges have been made, the cofactor of a_{rs} has turned into the minor. But every interchange of two rows or two columns changes the sign of every term in the expansion (and therefore of the cofactor of a_{rs}). Hence, B_{rs} changes sign $r + s - 2$ times, or, what amounts to the same thing, $r + s$ times, and thereby turns into A_{rs}. Hence:

$$B_{rs} = (-1)^{r+s} A_{rs}. \tag{1.5}$$

Thus, a determinant can be expanded in terms of the elements in one column (or row) and their minors.

PROBLEM 1.6. Expand the standard fourth-order determinant $|a_{ij}|$ by making use of minors, expanding these in turn, and check the answer against that of Problem 1.2.

1.5. Systems of Linear Equations

Next, we shall show how a system of n linear algebraic equations in n unknowns can be solved in terms of determinants. Consider the system

$$
\begin{aligned}
a_{11}x_1 + a_{12}x_2 + a_{13}x_3 + \ldots\ldots + a_{1n}x_n &= y_1 \\
a_{21}x_1 + a_{22}x_2 + a_{23}x_3 + \ldots\ldots + a_{2n}x_n &= y_2 \\
a_{31}x_1 + a_{32}x_2 + a_{33}x_3 + \ldots\ldots + a_{3n}x_n &= y_3 \\
\cdots\cdots\cdots\cdots\cdots\cdots\cdots\cdots\cdots\cdots\cdots \\
\cdots\cdots\cdots\cdots\cdots\cdots\cdots\cdots\cdots\cdots\cdots \\
a_{n1}x_1 + a_{n2}x_2 + a_{n3}x_3 + \ldots\ldots + a_{nn}x_n &= y_n
\end{aligned} \tag{1.6}
$$

These equations are to be solved for the unknowns x_j. As before, we shall write $|a_{ij}|$ for the determinant

$$
\begin{vmatrix}
a_{11} & a_{12} & a_{13}\ldots\ldots a_{1n} \\
a_{21} & a_{22} & a_{23}\ldots\ldots a_{2n} \\
a_{31} & a_{32} & a_{33}\ldots\ldots a_{3n} \\
\cdots & \cdots & \cdots\cdots\cdots\cdots \\
\cdots & \cdots & \cdots\cdots\cdots\cdots \\
a_{n1} & a_{n2} & a_{n3}\ldots\ldots a_{nn}
\end{vmatrix}
$$

Also as before, we shall write B_{rs} for the cofactor of the element a_{rs}. Equation (1.4) gives the expansion of the determinant $|a_{ij}|$ in terms of the elements of one row and their cofactors. By Theorem 1.4, we may similarly expand the determinant in terms of the elements of one column:

$$|a_{ij}| = \sum_{r=1}^{n} a_{rs}B_{rs}. \tag{1.7}$$

From this equation, it follows that the expression

$$\sum_{r=1}^{n} a_{rj}B_{rs}$$

with $j \neq s$ represents a determinant which is obtained from $|a_{ij}|$ by replacing the elements of the sth column respectively with those of the jth column. But such a determinant has two identical columns and therefore vanishes, by Theorem 1.3. In symbols:

$$\sum_{r=1}^{n} a_{rj}B_{rs} = \begin{cases} |a_{ij}| & \text{when } j = s, \\ 0 & \text{when } j \neq s. \end{cases} \tag{1.8}$$

Now, to return to Eqs. (1.6), let us multiply both sides of the rth equation by B_{rs} for all r, that is, the first by B_{1s}, the second by B_{2s}, and so on, and let us then add all the equations. We obtain:

$$x_1 \sum_{r=1}^{n} a_{r1}B_{rs} + x_2 \sum_{r=1}^{n} a_{r2}B_{rs} + x_3 \sum_{r=1}^{n} a_{r3}B_{rs} + \ldots$$

$$\ldots + x_n \sum_{r=1}^{n} a_{rn}B_{rs} = \sum_{r=1}^{n} y_r B_{rs}. \tag{1.9}$$

By Eqs. (1.8), this reduces to

$$|a_{ij}| x_s = \sum_{r=1}^{n} y_r B_{rs}. \tag{1.10}$$

This may be solved for x_s, provided that $|a_{ij}| \neq 0$:

$$x_s = \frac{\sum_{r=1}^{n} y_r B_{rs}}{|a_{ij}|}. \tag{1.11}$$

Thus, we can solve the Eqs. (1.6) for the x_s's. In the right-hand member of Eq. (1.11), both the numerator and the denominator may be written as determinants. The determinant in the numerator may be obtained from that in the denominator by replacing the elements in the sth column respectively by the y_r's.

Equation (1.11) is of doubtful practical value for solving Eqs. (1.6), since the determinants are usually quite laborious to evaluate. However, it is of theoretical interest, as we shall see presently.

THEOREM 1.8. Consider now the case where $y_1 = y_2 = y_3 = \ldots y_n = 0$. In this case, it follows from Eq. (1.11) that Eqs. (1.6) are satisfied by the solution $x_1 = x_2 = x_3 = \ldots = x_n = 0$. Nonzero solutions of Eqs. (1.6) are then possible if and only if $|a_{ij}| = 0$.

In this case, one of the x_j's may be chosen arbitrarily and the equations solved for the others, which are proportional to the former.

PROBLEM 1.7. The proof is left as an exercise for the reader. It is here assumed that the determinant $|a_{ij}|$ possesses at least one first minor which does not vanish. Otherwise, two or more of the x_j's may be chosen arbitrarily.

Finally, we derive the condition that n equations in $n - 1$ unknowns are satisfied by the same values of the unknowns. We then say that the equations are compatible. In Eqs. (1.6), let all the y_i's be equal to zero. We have already shown that these equations can have nonzero solutions only if $|a_{ij}| = 0$ and that one of the x_j's may then be chosen arbitrarily. Let us then choose $x_n = 1$. With this choice, Eqs. (1.6) do become n equations in $n - 1$ unknowns, and the condition that they be compatible is $|a_{ij}| = 0$. In other words:

THEOREM 1.9. The n equations in $n - 1$ unknowns

$$
\begin{aligned}
a_{11}x_1 + a_{12}x_2 + a_{13}x_3 + \ldots\ldots + a_{1,n-1}x_{n-1} + a_{1,n} &= 0 \\
a_{21}x_1 + a_{22}x_2 + a_{23}x_3 + \ldots\ldots + a_{2,n-1}x_{n-1} + a_{2,n} &= 0 \\
\ldots\ldots\ldots\ldots\ldots\ldots\ldots\ldots\ldots\ldots\ldots\ldots\ldots\ldots\ldots\ldots\ldots\ldots\ldots\ldots & \quad (1.12) \\
a_{n1}x_1 + a_{n2}x_2 + a_{n3}x_3 + \ldots\ldots + a_{n,n-1}x_{n-1} + a_{n,n} &= 0.
\end{aligned}
$$

are compatible only if $|a_{ij}| = 0$.

CHAPTER II

Nomograms

2.1. Fundamentals

A nomogram or alignment chart consists of three scales, not necessarily rectilinear. When a straight line is drawn across the diagram, it intersects the three scales in three numbers which are related according to some prescribed equation. The task of the nomographer is to construct the scales, given the equation. Nomograms involving more than three variables are essentially combinations of nomograms of three variables each and will be discussed later. The invention of nomograms is due to M. d'Ocagne, whose work is mainly the basis of this chapter and the next.

Let u, v, and w denote the three variables. It is most convenient to regard the three scales as curves whose equations are written in parametric form. Cartesian (rectangular) coordinates x, y are used unless otherwise stated. (Actually, the technique of nomography is not changed significantly if oblique coordinate axes are used.) The parametric equations of the scale for u, for instance, give x and y as functions of u. When u is given, the corresponding values of x and y can be calculated. Thus, for every value of u, a point of the scale can be plotted. The values of u are chosen at convenient intervals, and the plotted points are connected by a smooth curve. Similarly for v and w.

Let A, B, and C be the intersections of an arbitrary straight line with the scales for u, v, and w, respectively. The coordi-

13

nates of these three points will be distinguished by subscripts. The condition that the three points lie on the same straight line may be expressed analytically with the aid of Fig. 2.1.

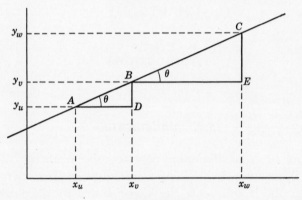

Figure 2.1

Let the point x_v, y_u be denoted by D, and x_w, y_v by E. We have

$$AD = x_v - x_u, \tag{2.1}$$

$$DB = y_v - y_u. \tag{2.2}$$

Let the inclination of the line ABC (the angle BAD or CBE) be denoted by θ.

Then

$$\tan \theta = \frac{DB}{AD} = \frac{y_v - y_u}{x_v - x_u}. \tag{2.3}$$

Similarly

$$\tan \theta = \frac{EC}{BE} = \frac{y_w - y_v}{x_w - x_v}. \tag{2.4}$$

Equating the two expressions for $\tan \theta$ gives

$$\frac{y_v - y_u}{x_v - x_u} = \frac{y_w - y_v}{x_w - x_v}. \tag{2.5}$$

Clearing of fractions and rearranging, we obtain

$$y_u x_v + y_v x_w + y_w x_u - y_u x_w - y_v x_u - y_w x_v = 0. \qquad (2.6)$$

This may be written in determinant notation thus:

$$\begin{vmatrix} y_u & x_u & 1 \\ y_v & x_v & 1 \\ y_w & x_w & 1 \end{vmatrix} = 0. \qquad (2.7)$$

Now, if x_u and y_u are functions of u only, x_v and y_v of v only, and x_w and y_w of w only, Eq. (2.7) represents a nomogram. The parametric equations for the scales are obtained by equating x_u, y_u, etc. to the appropriate functions. Equation (2.7) is the condition that the three points corresponding to three values u, v, w, lie on a straight line. (They are said to be *collinear*.) Any equation relating u, v, and w which can be written in the form of Eq. (2.7) can be nomographed.

To nomograph a given equation, we must first write it in the form

$$\begin{vmatrix} a_u & b_u & c_u \\ a_v & b_v & c_v \\ a_w & b_w & c_w \end{vmatrix} = 0, \qquad (2.8)$$

where the elements of each row depend on one of the three variables only. This is easier than to proceed at once to the form (2.7), as will be shown below. It may happen that some of the c's are equal to zero. In that case, we add the corresponding elements of one of the other columns to them. According to Theorem 1.7, this leaves the determinant unchanged. Next, we divide all the elements of the first row by c_u. According to Theorem 1.5, this has the effect of dividing the determinant by c_u. But in Eq. (2.8), the determinant is equated to zero, and zero divided by any finite number equals zero. (Why did we have to make sure that none of the c's were equal to zero?) Hence the division by c_u leaves the meaning of the equation unchanged. Similarly, we divide all the elements of the second row by c_v and those of the third row by c_w. The resulting equation is of the form (2.7).

Equation (2.5) and the subsequent steps above remain valid when oblique instead of rectangular coordinates are used. The only important change is that $(DB)/(AD)$ is then no longer equal to tan θ. However, it is still true that $(DB)/(AD) = (EC)/(BE)$, since the triangles ADB and BEC are similar.

PROBLEM 2.1. The details of the proof are left as an exercise for the student.

2.2. Nomogram for Addition

The method for rearranging a given equation in the form (2.8) is best explained with the aid of an example. Let us try to nomograph the equation

$$w = u + v. \tag{2.9}$$

This must first be rearranged in the form

$$u + v - w = 0, \tag{2.10}$$

that is, the right-hand member of the equation must be zero. The left-hand member must now be written in the required determinant form. At first sight, it seems as if a bewildering variety of possibilities must be tried. Actually, Theorem 1.2 allows us to throw out most of these possibilities as unnecessary repetitions of the others. For instance, it is immaterial which row depends on which of the three variables, just so long as each row depends on only one variable and no two rows depend on the same variable. Hence, we arbitrarily write functions of u in the first row, those of v in the second row, and those o w in the third row.

Likewise, by Theorem 1.2, the interchange of two columns will only change the sign of the determinant; and since the determinant is equated to zero, this change of sign has no effect. Now, from the form of Eq. (2.10), we expect one of the elements of the first row to equal u. (The other elements of the first row will be either 1 or 0.) Likewise, we expect one of the elements of the second row to be v, and one in the third row, w. The following possibilities must therefore be explored. The u

in the first row may be placed in the first, second, or third column. The same is true of the v in the second row and of the w in the third row. For each position of the u there are thus three possible positions for the v. This makes a total of 3^2 possible positions of the u and v combined. For each of these, there exist three possible positions of the w in the third row, making a total of 3^3 or 27 possibilities to be explored. But since the interchange of two columns does not affect the meaning of the equation, we may throw out most of these possibilities from the start. We may arbitrarily place u in the first column, since it can be moved to any other position by an interchange of columns. As for v, it may be placed either in the same column as u or in one of the others (two possibilities). If u and v are in the same column, w may be either in that column or in one of the others (two possibilities). Only if u and v are not in the same column are there three possible positions for the w which deserve our consideration. The possibilities to be investigated are therefore as follows:

$$P_1 = \begin{vmatrix} u & & \\ v & & \\ w & & \end{vmatrix}, \qquad P_2 = \begin{vmatrix} u & & \\ v & & \\ & w & \end{vmatrix}, \left.\vphantom{\begin{matrix}1\\1\\1\\1\\1\\1\end{matrix}}\right\}$$

$$P_3 = \begin{vmatrix} u & & \\ & v & \\ w & & \end{vmatrix}, \quad P_4 = \begin{vmatrix} u & & \\ & v & \\ & w & \end{vmatrix}, \quad P_5 = \begin{vmatrix} u & & \\ & v & \\ & & w \end{vmatrix}. \tag{2.11}$$

All of these possibilities with the exception of P_1 will be found wrong by a simple line of reasoning. For instance, in the expansion of P_2, there can be no more than two terms containing w. Each of these will contain one of the as yet undetermined elements from the third column. If these elements are not zero, the expansion of the determinant will contain the products uw and vw, which are uncalled for in Eq. (2.10); but if they are zero, the resulting equation will not contain w at all, again in disagreement with Eq. (2.10). The same argument applies to v in P_3 and to u in P_4.

PROBLEM 2.2. The reader should supply the details of each proof as an exercise.

As for P_5, its expansion must inevitably contain the term uvw, which is uncalled for by Eq. (2.10).

As for P_1, the missing elements of the determinant are easily determined by trial and error. There is more than one possible solution. We give just two examples:

$$\begin{vmatrix} u & 0 & 1 \\ v & 1 & 0 \\ w & 1 & 1 \end{vmatrix} = 0 \tag{2.12}$$

and

$$\begin{vmatrix} u & 0 & 1 \\ v & 1 & -1 \\ w & 1 & 0 \end{vmatrix} = 0. \tag{2.13}$$

Starting with Eq. (2.12), we proceed to reduce it to the form of Eq. (2.7) as described above. Since some of the elements of the third column are zero, we add to them respectively the elements of the second column. The result is

$$\begin{vmatrix} u & 0 & 1 \\ v & 1 & 1 \\ w & 1 & 2 \end{vmatrix} = 0. \tag{2.14}$$

The first and second row already have unity in the third column. Dividing the elements of the third row by 2, we obtain

$$\begin{vmatrix} u & 0 & 1 \\ v & 1 & 1 \\ {}^1/_2w & {}^1/_2 & 1 \end{vmatrix} = 0, \tag{2.15}$$

which is of the form of Eq. (2.7).

PROBLEM 2.3. As an exercise, the student may expand the determinant in Eq. (2.15) to convince himself that the result is in agreement with Eq. (2.10).

From Eq. (2.15), we obtain at once the parametric equations of the three scales:

$$y_u = u, \qquad x_u = 0,$$
$$y_v = v, \qquad x_v = 1, \qquad (2.16)$$
$$v_w = {}^1/_2w, \qquad x_w = {}^1/_2.$$

The resulting nomogram is plotted in Fig. 2.2. The three scales are parallel. This type of nomogram is widely used.

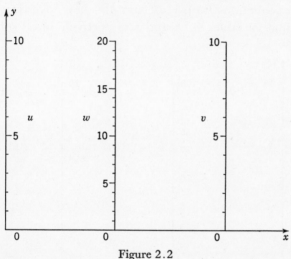

Figure 2.2

Another nomogram representing Eq. (2.10) may be obtained from Eq. (2.13).

PROBLEM 2.4. The reduction to the standard form, Eq. (2.7), is left as an exercise for the reader.

It would, however, be useless to add the elements of the second column respectively to those in the third, since this would still give rise to a zero element in the third column. Instead, we may add the elements of the first column respectively to those of the third. The nomogram obtained is not identical with Fig. 2.2, although it represents the same equation. Still other variants could have been obtained from Eq. (2.12) if the columns had been rearranged. We shall not dwell further on this subject here, since we shall study it systematically in later chapters.

The method which we have just described is not altered materially if the three variables u, v, and w in Eq. (2.9) are replaced with three functions, each depending on a different variable. Thus we can nomograph an equation of the form

$$f(w) = g(u) + h(v). \qquad (2.17)$$

The three functions $f(w)$, $g(u)$, and $h(v)$ now take the places of the original variables w, u, and v respectively in all subsequent

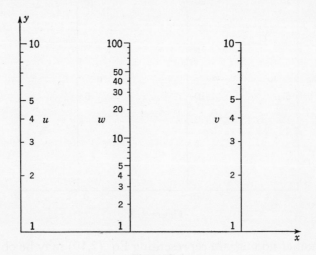

Figure 2.3

equations through Eqs. (2.16). Of particular practical value is the substitution

$$\left.\begin{aligned} f(w) &= \log w, \\ g(u) &= \log u, \\ h(v) &= \log v. \end{aligned}\right\} \qquad (2.18)$$

Instead of Eqs. (2.16) we now obtain

$$\left.\begin{aligned} y_u &= \log u, & x_u &= 0, \\ y_v &= \log v, & x_v &= 1, \\ y_w &= \tfrac{1}{2}\log w, & x_w &= \tfrac{1}{2}; \end{aligned}\right\} \qquad (2.19)$$

and instead of Eq. (2.9), we obtain

$$\log w = \log u + \log v, \tag{2.20}$$

whence

$$w = uv. \tag{2.21}$$

Thus, by plotting Eqs. (2.19), we obtain a nomogram for multiplication. This is shown in Fig. 2.3. It is also widely used. Note that the graduations on the scales are now no longer regularly spaced.

PROBLEM 2.5. Nomograph the equation $1/w = 1/u + 1/v$. If w is the focal length of a lens, and u is the distance of an object from the lens, then an image is formed at a distance v from the lens. Or, if u and v are two resistances in parallel, then w is their combined resistance. Or, if u and v are two capacitances in series, then w is their combined capacitance.

PROBLEM 2.6. Nomograph the equation $w^2 = u^2 + v^2$. According to the theorem of Pythagoras, u, v, and w are the sides of a right-angled triangle, w being the hypotenuse.

2.3. Another Nomogram for Multiplication

Our next example is Eq. (2.21) nomographed without the aid of logarithms. As before, we rearrange the equation so that the right-hand member of the equation is zero:

$$uv - w = 0. \tag{2.22}$$

We proceed by trial and error as before. However, the following short cuts are to be noted. Any arrangements with u and v in the same column are not worth trying, since then the product uv will not appear. Likewise, w should be in the same column with either u or v, since otherwise the product uvw must inevitably appear. In view of what we said in the preceding section about interchange of rows and columns, we need only try the two possibilities

$$\begin{vmatrix} u & 1 & 0 \\ 0 & v & 1 \\ -w & 0 & 1 \end{vmatrix} = 0 \tag{2.23a}$$

and
$$
\begin{vmatrix}
u & 0 & -1 \\
1 & v & 0 \\
0 & w & 1
\end{vmatrix} = 0. \tag{2.23b}
$$

We have proceeded at once to write in the constant elements. These are not unique, as we pointed out in the preceding section.

Either of Eqs. (2.23) may be brought into the form of Eq. (2.7) by the same method as before.

PROBLEM 2.7. The details are left as an exercise for the reader.

From Eq. (2.23a) we obtain

$$
\begin{vmatrix}
+u & 1 & 1 \\
0 & \dfrac{v}{v+1} & 1 \\
-w & 0 & 1
\end{vmatrix} = 0, \tag{2.24}
$$

from which the parametric equations of the three scales can be written by inspection. The reader should learn to do this in

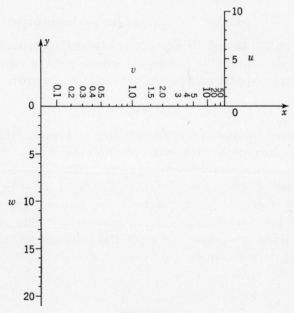

Figure 2.4

his head. The resulting nomogram is shown in Fig. 2.4. This type is widely used. Curiously enough, the scales for u and v are not alike. The u scale is graduated at regular intervals; the v scale is not. This is surprising, since an interchange of u and v will leave Eq. (2.21) unchanged.

Here as before, the variables u, v, and w may be replaced with arbitrary functions.

PROBLEM 2.8. As an exercise, the reader may construct a nomogram for the equation $(u + 1)v = w$.

Constants occurring in an equation can usually be combined with one or more of the variables to form functions. For instance, Mach number M is given in terms of velocity V, absolute temperature T, and two constants $\gamma = 1.40$ and $R = 2.869 \times 10^6$ by the equation

$$M = \frac{V}{\sqrt{\gamma R T}} . \tag{2.25}$$

This may be rearranged into the form

$$V = M\sqrt{\gamma R T}. \tag{2.26}$$

Now, let us write

$$\left. \begin{aligned} u &= M, \\ v &= \sqrt{\gamma R T}, \\ w &= V. \end{aligned} \right\} \tag{2.27}$$

Since γ and R are constants, v is a function of T only. Equation (2.26) may therefore be nomographed in either of the forms of Figs. 2.3 and 2.4.

PROBLEM 2.9. Nomograph the equation $w = (u - v)/(u + v)$. Here w is the reflectance of a surface separating two media of refractive indices u and v. Reflectance is the ratio of amplitudes of the reflected and incident light waves. The same equation applies to electric waves reflected at the junction between two transmission lines of characteristic admittances u and v.

The illustrative examples given so far all lead to a nomogram with three rectilinear scales. The following examples lead to a nomogram with one curved scale:

PROBLEM 2.10. Nomograph the equation

$$p^2 = q^2 + r^2 - 2qr \cos \theta,$$

with q a constant.   Here p, q, and r are the sides of a triangle, p being opposite the angle θ.

PROBLEM 2.11. Nomograph the equation

$$P = \frac{1}{R^2 e^{\alpha R}},$$

where e is the base of natural logarithms (a constant).

Hint: Take logarithms to base e of both sides.

Consider a point light source of unit intensity immersed in a medium of coefficient of absorption α.   Then the light intensity at a distance R from the source equals P.

The following example leads to a nomogram with two curved scales.

PROBLEM 2.12. Nomograph the equation

$$uv + uw + \sin v + \cos w = 0,$$

with v and w in radians.

The following example leads to a nomogram with three curved scales.

PROBLEM 2.13. Nomograph the equation

$$u^2 v^2 + v^3 w^2 + wu - wv^2 - v^3 u - u^2 w^2 = 0.$$

The following leads to a nomogram with three rectilinear scales.

PROBLEM 2.14. Nomograph the equation

$$u = \frac{vw}{1 + (v - 1)w}.$$

2.4. Circular Nomograms

As a last example, we nomograph the quadratic equation in q:

$$q^2 - aq + b = 0. \tag{2.28}$$

PROBLEM 2.15. The details are left as an exercise for the reader.

Brought into the form of Eq. (2.7), it becomes

$$\begin{vmatrix} \dfrac{q^2}{q-1} & \dfrac{q}{q-1} & 1 \\ a & 1 & 1 \\ b & 0 & 1 \end{vmatrix} = 0. \qquad (2.29)$$

From this, the reader may construct the nomogram. The scale for q is a hyperbola. (The reader should save this nomogram for reference in the next chapter.)

A straight line through two points on the a and b scales may intersect the q scale in two points. In that case, Eq. (2.28) has two real solutions. Or the straight line may be tangent to the q scale. In that case, the two solutions are equal. Finally, the straight line may not intersect the q scale at all. In that case, the two solutions are complex.

PROBLEM 2.16. The student should find an example of each as an exercise. How can this be done by calculation only, without construction of the actual nomogram?

Let the two solutions of Eq. (2.28) be denoted by q_1 and q_2. Then

$$(q - q_1)(q - q_2) = 0. \qquad (2.30)$$

Multiplying out the parentheses, we obtain

$$q^2 - (q_1 + q_2)q + q_1q_2 = 0. \qquad (2.31)$$

Comparing this to Eq. (2.28), we see that

$$a = q_1 + q_2 \qquad (2.32)$$

and

$$b = q_1q_2. \qquad (2.33)$$

We have previously obtained nomograms for addition and multiplication. We shall now obtain some more. The variables q_1 and q_2 are plotted on one and the same scale. If the scale for b is omitted, the result represents Eq. (2.32), which is Eq. (2.9), except for the notation. It may be represented in determinant notation as follows. In Eq. (2.29), the row involving q is written twice, but with subscripts 1 and 2, respectively. The row involving b is omitted. The result is

$$\begin{vmatrix} \dfrac{q_1^2}{q_1 - 1} & \dfrac{q_1}{q_1 - 1} & 1 \\[2ex] \dfrac{q_2^2}{q_2 - 1} & \dfrac{q_2}{q_2 - 1} & 1 \\[2ex] a & 1 & 1 \end{vmatrix} = 0. \tag{2.34}$$

PROBLEM 2.17. As an exercise, the student should expand the determinant and show that the result agrees with Eq. (2.32). It may be obtained in the form

$$a(q_2 - q_1) = (q_2 + q_1)(q_2 - q_1). \tag{2.35}$$

Of course, this will yield Eq. (2.32) when the factor $q_2 - q_1$ is canceled out on both sides. However, in this case, Eq. (2.35) can be nomographed as it stands, without cancellation of the common factor, and the result is not the same as Fig. 2.2.

By substitution of logarithms in place of the original variables in Eq. (2.32), we obtain a nomogram for multiplication. Another nomogram for multiplication is obtained by omitting the row involving a from Eq. (2.29) and repeating the row involving q, with a distinguishing subscript, as before. The result is

$$\begin{vmatrix} \dfrac{q_1^2}{q_1 - 1} & \dfrac{q_1}{q_1 - 1} & 1 \\[2ex] \dfrac{q_2^2}{q_2 - 1} & \dfrac{q_2}{q_2 - 1} & 1 \\[2ex] b & 0 & 1 \end{vmatrix} = 0. \tag{2.36}$$

PROBLEM 2.18. Again, the student should expand the determinant as an exercise.

Again, a multiplicative factor appears on both sides of Eq. (2.33). We shall see in the next chapter that the hyperbolic scale for q can be transformed into a circle. For this reason, the nomograms represented by Eqs. (2.34) and (2.36) are called circular nomograms. They are the invention of J. Clark, who is also the inventor of some of the nomograms discussed in Chapter VIII.

2.5. Semideductive Method

The above method for arranging a given equation in the form of Eq. (2.8) is deductive provided those of the determinant elements which depend on the variables u, v, and w (that is, all those elements which are not constants) can be inferred from the form of the equation. To the extent to which any elements of the determinant must be inferred by inspection, this method of nomography involves trial and error. In rare instances, it may be required to nomograph an equation for which the elements in one row of the determinant (that is, those depending on only one of the three variables) are easy enough to infer by inspection, while those in the other two rows are fairly complicated functions which are far from obvious. In this case, the given equation may be arranged in the form of Eq. (2.8) by the following method.

Let a_u, b_u, c_u be those elements of the determinant which can be inferred by inspection, and let the given equation be written in the form

$$a_u F(v, w) + b_u G(v, w) + c_u H(v, w) = 0. \tag{2.37}$$

Let us write

$$\xi = \frac{F(v, w)}{H(v, w)}, \tag{2.38}$$

$$\eta = \frac{G(v, w)}{H(v, w)}. \tag{2.39}$$

Let w and v in turn be eliminated between Eqs. (2.38) and (2.39). A nomogram is possible if the resulting equations are linear in ξ and η. Together with Eq. (2.37), rewritten in the notation of Eqs. (2.38) and (2.39), these will then form a system of the form

$$a_u\xi + b_u\eta + c_u = 0, \qquad (2.40)$$

$$a_v\xi + b_v\eta + c_v = 0, \qquad (2.41)$$

$$a_w\xi + b_w\eta + c_w = 0. \qquad (2.42)$$

According to Theorem 1.9, these three equations will be compatible if and only if Eq. (2.8) is satisfied.   The result is straightforward.   The use of this method is rarely necessary.

PROBLEM 2.19. As an exercise, the reader may nomograph

$$(1 + L)h^2 - Lh(1 + p) - \tfrac{1}{3}(1 - L)(1 + 2p) = 0, \quad (2.43)$$

the elements of the first row being h^2, h, 1.

In this case, it is unlikely that any of the elements of the other rows could have been inferred by inspection.

Unfortunately, this method is rarely useful.   For instance, it would fail if applied to Eq. (2.10) or (2.21).   This is unimportant, since these problems are easily solved by trial and error, as we saw.   However, a more serious objection will be seen if this method is used for solving Problem 2.13 above.   If we take v^2, v^3, and 1 for the elements of the first row, Eqs. (2.38) and (2.39) will of course involve u and w instead of v and w. Their elimination now involves the solution of a quadratic equation and substitution of this solution into quite a complicated expression.   While this is possible, it is excessively laborious.   If we had taken u^2, u, and 1 as the elements of the first row, the elimination of v between Eqs. (2.38) and (2.39) would have involved the solution of a cubic equation.   It is not difficult to construct examples which will lead to transcendental equations.   Such problems can usually be solved by the method of Chapter VII.   This however, requires a knowledge of calculus.

PROBLEM 2.20. Write the equation

$$\frac{1}{u} + \frac{w}{v} = f(v)$$

in determinant notation preparatory to nomographing. $f(v)$ is an arbitrary function of v.

CHAPTER III

Projective Transformations

3.1. Elementary Transformations

Any transformation which transforms any point into a point and any straight line into a straight line will transform a nomogram into another nomogram representing the same equation. The result of a transformation is called the *transform* of the given figure. Let us enumerate these transformations. The original cartesian coordinates are denoted by x and y, the transformed coordinates, by x' and y'.

Translation of Axes

Let the origin of the unprimed system be at a, b with respect to the primed system (Fig. 3.1). Then

$$x' = x + a, \tag{3.1}$$

$$v' = y + b. \tag{3.2}$$

This transformation changes only the position of the nomogram and not its form.

Rotation of Axes

Let the unprimed axes make an angle θ with respect to the primed axes, with θ positive if the primed axes have to be

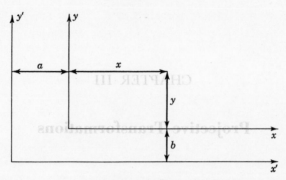

Figure 3.1

rotated in a counterclockwise direction to be brought into coincidence with the unprimed axes (Fig. 3.2). Then:

$$y' = x \sin \theta + y \cos \theta, \qquad (3.3)$$

$$x' = x \cos \theta - y \sin \theta. \qquad (3.4)$$

PROBLEM 3.1. The details of the proof should be supplied by the reader with the aid of Fig. 3.2. Rotation, like translation, changes only the position and does not change the form of the nomogram.

PROBLEM 3.2. Solve Eqs. (3.3) and (3.4) for x and y in terms of x' and y'. These are the equations for the inverse transformation. Once more, starting from the original Eqs.

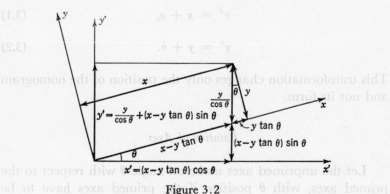

Figure 3.2

(3.3) and (3.4), change the sign of θ. How are the resulting equations related to those derived for the inverse transformation? Why?

Stretch

Let

$$x' = ax, \tag{3.5}$$

$$y' = y. \tag{3.6}$$

If $a > +1$, then the figure plotted with respect to the primed axes is stretched in the x direction. If $0 < a < +1$, the same transformation represents a contraction in the x direction. If $a < 0$, we have a stretch or contraction combined with a reflection in the y axis. The transformation equations for stretch and contraction in the y direction will probably be obvious to the reader. The transformation equations for stretch in any other direction are not important to us. The interested reader may derive them as an exercise. Alternatively, the figure may first be rotated so that the desired direction of stretch is aligned with one of the coordinate axes. The above method of stretch may then be used.

PROBLEM 3.3. Derive the transformation equations for stretch in any direction not parallel to a coordinate axis.

Shear

Let the original figure be plotted in terms of oblique coordinates x, y, and let the angle between the positive x and y axes be $90° - \theta$. The resulting figure may be described with respect to a rectangular (primed) coordinate system. Let the y and y' axes coincide. Then (Fig. 3.3):

$$x' = x \cos \theta, \tag{3.7}$$

$$y' = y + x \sin \theta. \tag{3.8}$$

It is possible to obtain the same transformation by successive stretch and contraction in two different directions followed by

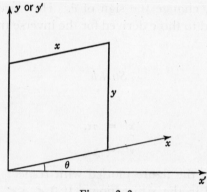

Figure 3.3

a rotation. The details are not important to us, but the interested reader may work them out as an exercise.

PROBLEM 3.4. Prove that shear is equivalent to successive stretch and contraction in two different directions followed by a rotation.

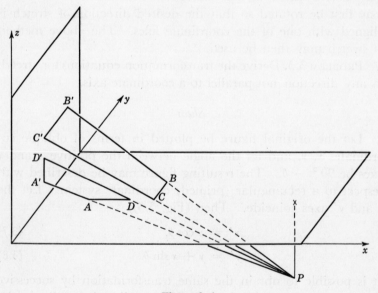

Figure 3.4

3.2. *Projection*

This is perhaps the most powerful tool for our purposes. Figure 3.4 will be used for a preliminary qualitative explanation. In a space of three dimensions, rectangular coordinates x, y, z are used. The figure to be transformed is drawn on the xy plane, which is supposed transparent. A point source of light P is placed below the xy plane. A shadow of the figure in the xy plane will then be projected onto the yz plane. With the aid of such a figure, the reader will be able to visualize how, by projection, a line segment may be foreshortened (like AD) or magnified (like CB), depending on its position and orientation. The point P is called the center of perspectivity. In the limiting case where P is at an infinite distance from the figure to be projected, the projecting rays become parallel, and projection is tantamount to a stretch or contraction, possibly combined with a shear. For this reason, all the transformations discussed in this chapter are loosely called projective transformations. Some authors prefer the term "homographic transformations," whereas others use this term with a different meaning.

Note the construction in Fig. 3.4. A straight line is drawn through the center of perspectivity P and the point A to be projected. It is prolonged to its intersection with the plane onto which the figure is to be projected. The intersection A' is the transform of the point A.

This construction remains valid in the case of Fig. 3.5, where P is located between A and A', even though one would hardly regard A as an object and A' as its shadow. Otherwise, it would be necessary to prolong the light ray PA' backward through the light source P to the object A. If the reader prefers an optical interpretation of Fig. 3.5, he may suppose a large, diffuse light source below the xy plane, and he may regard P as the pinhole of a pinhole camera.

From Fig. 3.5, the transformation equations can be derived. Let $\bar{x}$, $\bar{y}$, $\bar{z}$ be the coordinates of the center of perspectivity P, and let x, y, 0 be the coordinates of the untransformed point A. The coordinates of the transform A' might be denoted by 0, y', z. However, for the sake of consistency with the transformations discussed above, it is more convenient to write x' in place of z. Let the point $\bar{x}$, y, 0 be denoted by B, let 0, y', 0 be denoted by C, let $\bar{x}$, y, 0 be denoted by D, and let 0, y, 0 be denoted by E.

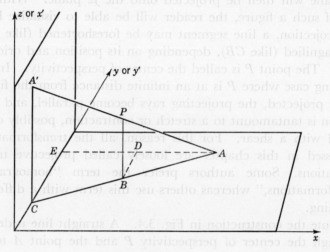

Figure 3.5

PROBLEM 3.5. The reader may prove as an exercise that the triangles $A'CA$ and PBA are similar.

Since the triangles $A'CA$ and PBA are similar,

$$\frac{A'C}{PB} = \frac{CA}{BA}.$$

(3.9)

Furthermore, the triangles CEA and BDA are similar. (Why?) Hence

$$\frac{CA}{BA} = \frac{EA}{DA} = \frac{CE}{BD}.$$

(3.10)

From Eqs. (3.9) and (3.10), we have

$$\frac{A'C}{PB} = \frac{EA}{DA} = \frac{CE}{BD}. \tag{3.11}$$

Hence

$$\frac{x'}{\bar{z}} = \frac{x}{x - \bar{x}} = \frac{y - y'}{y - \bar{y}}. \tag{3.12}$$

These may be solved for x' and y':

$$x' = \frac{x\bar{z}}{x - \bar{x}}, \tag{3.13}$$

$$y' = \frac{x\bar{y} - \bar{x}y}{x - \bar{x}}. \tag{3.14}$$

The projective transformation shown in Fig. 3.5 may seem to lack generality, since we have prescribed that the xy plane and the $x'y'$ plane must be mutually perpendicular. Actually, nothing significant would have been changed if this condition had been waived. In that case, we would simply have used oblique coordinates instead of rectangular coordinates.

PROBLEM 3.6. The details are left as an exercise for the reader.

We have said that a projective transformation transforms a point into a point and a straight line into a straight line. It may seem as if there is an exception to this rule. The line BD in Fig. 3.5, when transformed by projection, does not appear in the $x'y'$ plane, since the projecting rays are parallel to this plane. The same is true of any point on this line. We can avoid this difficulty by defining the concepts of a point or a straight line at infinity. There is only one straight line at infinity. Its direction has no meaning, since an angle may change its value under a projective transformation. A family of parallel lines intersect in a point at infinity. Under projection, they transform into a family of concurrent straight lines. All points at infinity lie on the line at infinity.

3.3. *Transformation of an Arbitrary Quadrilateral into a Rectangle*

When the nomographer is asked to nomograph an equation in three variables, he is usually told what range of values two of the three variables should cover. The range of values of the third variable will then follow from the given equation. But it is then frequently found that one of the three scales is ridiculously short compared to the others. This means a loss of accuracy, since the graduations on the short scale will be too

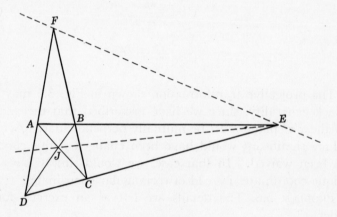

Figure 3.6

close together and cannot be read with sufficient accuracy. In that case, the short scale may be magnified and the long scales reduced at the same time by a projective transformation.

The problem of giving a given nomogram a convenient size and shape frequently takes the following form. A quadrilateral is drawn which serves as a sufficiently narrow frame around the nomogram. By the transformations described above (applied singly or in combination), this quadrilateral may be transformed into a rectangle. Let *ABCD* (Fig. 3.6) be the given quadrilateral. Let the sides *AB* and *CD* be prolonged to their point of intersection *E*, and let *AD* and *BC* be

prolonged to their point of intersection F.   Let the coordinate
axes be rotated so that the line EF is parallel to the y axis.   By
taking the x coordinate of the line EF as the value of $\bar{x}$, we
project EF (and therefore the points E and F) to infinity.
Hence $A'B'\|C'D'$ and $A'D'\|B'C'$, so that the quadrilateral
becomes a parallelogram.   Next, the coordinate axes are
rotated so that two sides of the parallelogram are parallel to a
coordinate axis.   The parallelogram may then be transformed
into a rectangle by a shear, and this rectangle may be given any
desired proportions by a stretch.

PROBLEM 3.7. As an exercise the student should obtain the
transformation equations for transforming the following quadrilateral into a square:

$$
\begin{aligned}
&A\ (2,7)\\
&B\ (4,6)\\
&C\ (5,2)\\
&D\ (1,1).
\end{aligned}
$$

The numbers in parentheses are the x and y coordinates of the
four corners of the quadrilateral.   The intermediate transforms
may be distinguished by two, three, etc. primes or by subscripts.
Finally, the intermediate stages should be eliminated by substitution in the transformation equations, so that a single pair
of transformation equations take us at once from the original
quadrilateral to the final square.

PROBLEM 3.8. Derive a transformation which will transform
the following trapezoid into a parallelogram:

$$
\begin{aligned}
&A\ (1,1)\\
&B\ (4,7)\\
&C\ (5,4)\\
&D\ (4,2).
\end{aligned}
$$

The applicability of this method has its limitations.   As an
example, consider the nomogram sketched schematically in
Fig. 3.7.   The scale for v, with end points C and D, is much
shorter than the other two scales and lies between them.   The

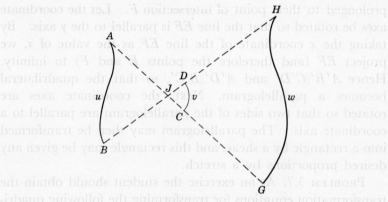

Figure 3.7

end points of the u scale are A and B, and those of the w scale
are G and H. If the ranges of values of u and v have been
prescribed, the range of values of w is determined by the equation to be nomographed, or it may be obtained graphically
from the nomogram itself, since the line AC must go through
G, and BD must go through H. (There may be exceptions
to this rule, since it may happen that w is multiple valued for
certain ranges of u and v.) It would not do any good to transform the quadrilateral $ABGH$ into a rectangle, since even after
such a transformation, the scale for v would be very short compared to the other two. Neither would it do any good to transform the quadrilateral $ABCD$ into a rectangle, since this would
magnify not only the v scale, but the w scale as well. A
more useful transformation may be inferred from Fig. 3.6. Let
J be the point of intersection of the diagonals AC and BD of
the quadrilateral $ABCD$. If the straight line JE is projected to
infinity, the points A, B, C, D transform into the corners of a
parallelogram, but in the order $ACDB$, going around the parallelogram. Finally, $ACDB$ may be transformed into a rectangle
as before. Whereas the order of the scales in Fig. 3.7 from left
to right is u, v, w, in the transformed nomogram, it will be v,
w, u. This transformation reduces all three scales to a reasonable size.

PROBLEM 3.9. As an exercise the reader should subject the quadrilateral of Problem 3.7 to this transformation.

Of course, this transformation is applicable only if the line to be projected to infinity does not intersect the useful portion of any scale. Otherwise, one point of that scale will be at infinity.

3.4. Discussion

The method of Section 3.2 is not always necessary. For instance, in Fig. 2.4, let u and w both range from 0 to 10. By a shear, this nomogram can be brought into the form sketched schematically in Fig. 3.8, which resembles a letter N. When

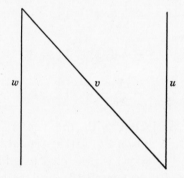

Figure 3.8

rotated counterclockwise through a right angle, it assumes the appearance of a letter Z. For this reason, this type of nomogram is variously called an N chart or a Z chart.

As another example of a projective transformation, consider the nomogram of the equation $1/w = 1/u + 1/v$, which was to be derived in Problem 2.5. By substituting $1/u$, $1/v$, and $1/w$ respectively in place of u, v, and w in Eq. (2.15), we can solve Problem 2.5. The nomogram is obtained from the equation

$$\begin{vmatrix} \dfrac{1}{u} & 0 & 1 \\[2ex] \dfrac{1}{v} & 1 & 1 \\[2ex] \dfrac{1}{2w} & \dfrac{1}{2} & 1 \end{vmatrix} = 0. \tag{3.15}$$

This may or may not be useful, depending on the ranges of values of u, v, and w to be covered. All three scales are graduated at unequal intervals, and the points $u = 0$, $v = 0$, and $w = 0$ all lie at infinity. Now by rotating and translating axes, we can arrange it that the present x axis becomes the line $x' = \bar{x}$. Omitting the prime in preparation for a further transformation, we obtain from Eq. (3.15) by this transformation

$$\begin{vmatrix} 0 & -\dfrac{1}{u} + \bar{x} & 1 \\[2ex] 1 & -\dfrac{1}{v} + \bar{x} & 1 \\[2ex] \dfrac{1}{2} & -\dfrac{1}{2w} + \bar{x} & 1 \end{vmatrix} = 0. \tag{3.16}$$

Now let this be projected with the center of perspectivity $P(\bar{x}, \bar{y}, \bar{z})$, so that the x axis of Eq. (3.15) (on which lie the points $u = \infty$, $v = \infty$, and $w = \infty$) is projected to infinity. Applying the transformation Equations (3.13) and (3.14) to the parametric equations for the v scale as derived from Eq. (3.16), we obtain:

$$x_v{}' = (1 - v\bar{x})\bar{z}, \tag{3.17}$$

$$y_v{}' = \bar{y} + \bar{x}v(1 - \bar{y}). \tag{3.18}$$

PROBLEM 3.10. The derivation of the corresponding equations for u and w is left as an exercise for the reader.

Note that Eqs. (3.17) and (3.18) are linear in v. As a result, the graduations on the v scale are placed at regular intervals. The same is true of the scales for u and w, and furthermore the values chosen for the constants $\bar{v}$ and $\bar{z}$ are immaterial, provided only that $\bar{z} \neq 0$. It is only necessary to project the scale marks $u = \infty$, $v = \infty$, and $w = \infty$ to infinity.

Perhaps the reader did not solve Problem 2.5 in this manner. The given equation could have been translated into determinant notation by trial and error, and perhaps not all nomographers would come out with the same result. For instance, in Eq. (3.15) let us multiply the elements of the first row by u, those of the second row by v, and those of the third row by $2w$, and let us interchange columns 1 and 3. The result is

$$\begin{vmatrix} u & 0 & 1 \\ v & v & 1 \\ 2w & w & 1 \end{vmatrix} = 0. \tag{3.19}$$

In Eqs. (3.17) and (3.18) and the corresponding equations for u and w, the reader should write $\bar{x} = \bar{z} = 1$, $\bar{y} = 0$. How is the result related to Eq. (3.19)? It frequently happens that two nomographers trying to nomograph the same equation arrive at two nomograms which are projective transforms of each other. However, it may also happen that two nomograms are obtained which are not so related. Figures 2.3 and 2.4 will serve as an example.

Problems 3.11 through 3.13 may be solved either by a completely analytical method, or else two scales may be obtained analytically while the third is obtained graphically. The choice between these two methods is left to the reader. The second method is usually easier.

PROBLEM 3.11. Nomograph Eq. (2.26) with $\gamma = 1.40$ and $R = 2.869 \times 10^6$. Let M range from 0 to 2.5 and T from 200 to 350. Here T is in °K, and V is in cm./sec. Arrange the resulting nomogram in a convenient rectangle.

PROBLEM 3.12. Solve the problem similar to 3.11 but with T ranging from 260 to 320, and V ranging from 5×10^3 to 6×10^4.

PROBLEM 3.13. Solve the problem similar to 3.11 but with M ranging from 0.5 to 4.0, and V ranging from 1.5×10^4 to 6×10^4.

PROBLEM 3.14. Prove that an interchange of u and v in Eq. (2.24) is not tantamount to a projective transformation.

Hint: Find a projective transformation which projects the straight line through the origin and the point $u = -1$ (that is $x = +1, y = -1$) to infinity. How close does this bring us to achieving the desired result? Is any other projection worth trying?

3.5. Transformation of the Circular Nomogram to the Standard Form

It sometimes happens that a scale has one or more points (other than the ends) at infinity, so that it consists of two branches. In that case, a connected scale may be obtained by a projective transformation. It is only necessary to draw any straight line which separates the two branches and to project this line to infinity. The q scale in Eqs. (2.29), (2.34), and (2.36) will serve as an illustrative example. It is described by the parametric equations.

$$x = \frac{q}{q - 1}, \tag{3.20}$$

$$v = \frac{q^2}{q - 1}. \tag{3.21}$$

Let q be eliminated between these. The result is

$$x^2 - xy + y = 0. \tag{3.22}$$

At this point, it would be convenient to make use of the following theorems.

THEOREM 3.1. Any equation quadratic in x and/or y represents a conic section (which may be degenerate).

THEOREM 3.2. A projective transformation transforms a conic section into a conic section.

THEOREM 3.3. An ellipse has no point at infinity. A parabola has one point at infinity. (It is tangent to the line at infinity.) A hyperbola has two points at infinity. (It intersects the line at infinity.)

The proofs of these theorems are perhaps more advanced than the prerequisites for this course. Unfortunately, their inclusion in this text would lead us too far afield. For the present application, the reader should at least be able to follow every step of the reasoning below as described.

We shall give the transformations only for Eq. (2.29), since Eqs. (2.34) and (2.36) follow from it as corollaries. Solving Eq. (3.22) for y, we obtain

$$y = \frac{x^2}{x-1}. \tag{3.23}$$

Hence, the curve represented by Eq. (3.22) has the line $x = 1$ as an asymptote. From this, we conclude that Eq. (3.22) represents a hyperbola.

Let us subject Eq. (2.29) to a rotation of coordinates, Eqs. (3.3) and (3.4), with $\theta = -45°$, so that $\sin \theta = -1/\sqrt{2}$, $\cos \theta = +1/\sqrt{2}$. At the same time, let us stretch the nomogram by a factor of $\sqrt{2}$ in both the x and y directions. Then Eqs. (3.3) and (3.4) become

$$y' = -x + y, \tag{3.24}$$

$$x' = +x + y, \tag{3.25}$$

whence Eq. (2.29) transforms into

$$\begin{vmatrix} q & \dfrac{q^2 + q}{q - 1} & 1 \\ a - 1 & a + 1 & 1 \\ b & b & 1 \end{vmatrix} = 0. \tag{3.26}$$

We shall presently transform this by projection with $\bar{x} = \bar{z} = +1, \bar{y} = -1$. But first we write out the parametric equations for the q scale and eliminate q between them. The result is

$$y^2 + y(1 - x) + x = 0. \tag{3.27}$$

It is the equation of a hyperbola. If it is to be solved for y, the discriminant is $x^2 - 6x + 1$. This is negative for $x = 1$.

In other words, the line $x = 1$ does not intersect the hyperbola but passes through the gap between the two branches. The proposed transformation projects this line to infinity, so that the hyperbola transforms into an ellipse (see Theorems 3.2 and 3.3). Equation (3.26) transforms into

$$\begin{vmatrix} \dfrac{-2q^2}{q^2 + 1} & \dfrac{q^2 + q}{q^2 + 1} & 1 \\[2ex] -2 & \dfrac{a + 1}{a} & 1 \\[2ex] \dfrac{-2b}{b - 1} & \dfrac{b}{b - 1} & 1 \end{vmatrix} = 0. \tag{3.28}$$

PROBLEM 3.15. If the reader had difficulty following the reasoning which led from Eq. (2.29) to Eq. (3.28), he may find it instructive to plot the nomograms represented by Eqs. (2.29), (3.26), and (3.28) and to sketch a perspective drawing similar to Fig. 3.5 illustrating the step from Eq. (3.26) to Eq. (3.28). In plotting these nomograms, be sure to use the same scale unit for both x and y and to make the scale such that portions of both branches of the hyperbolic q scale appear on the graph paper. It will be best to use the same scale unit for all three drawings. Instead of a perspective drawing, a three-dimensional model may be constructed.

The nomogram represented by Eq. (3.28) has the a scale parallel to the x axis. We shall subject it to a shear to make the b scale coincide with the y axis. Equations (3.7) and (3.8) cannot be used for this, since they leave the orientation of the y axis unchanged but rotate the x axis.

PROBLEM 3.16. The corresponding equations for the present transformation may be derived by the reader as an exercise.

Next, the figure is translated so that the point $b = \infty$ falls at the origin. Finally, the figure is stretched so that the elliptical scale becomes a circle.

PROBLEM 3.17. The details are left to the reader.

These three transformations may be combined into a single transformation described by the equations

$$y' = {}^1\!/_{2y} + 1, \tag{3.29}$$

$$x' = x + {}^1\!/_{2y}. \tag{3.30}$$

Equation (3.28) then transforms into

$$\begin{vmatrix} \dfrac{1}{q^2 + 1} & \dfrac{q}{q^2 + 1} & 1 \\[2ex] 0 & \dfrac{1}{a} & 1 \\[2ex] \dfrac{1}{1 - b} & 0 & 1 \end{vmatrix} = 0. \tag{3.31}$$

This is the desired result. The corresponding nomogram is shown in Fig. 3.9. This transformation of the q scale into a

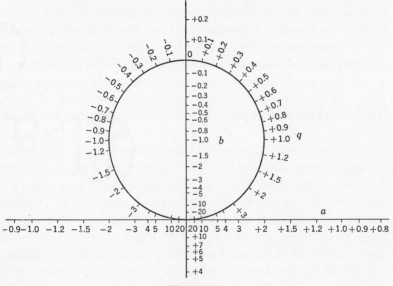

Figure 3.9

circle is not the only one possible, but it is generally preferred because of the simple form of the result.

The circular nomogram is not a mere mathematical freak, but may be of practical value. It has the useful property that two of the three variables (q_1 and q_2 in Eqs. (2.32) and (2.33)) are shown on a scale whose entire length from $-\infty$ to $+\infty$ lies in a finite portion of the plane. If only positive values of q_1 and q_2 are required in Eq. (2.33), we may write it in the form

$$q_1(-q_2) = -b. \qquad (3.32)$$

Now, the entire nomogram with values of q_1, q_2, and b ranging from 0 to ∞ lies in a finite portion of the plane.

Any equation which can be represented by a nomogram consisting of three straight-line scales can also be represented by a circular nomogram. Two cases may arise. The three scales either do or do not intersect in a single point. If they do, this point of intersection may be projected to infinity, so that the three scales become parallel. The nomogram obtained is then brought into coincidence with the nomogram of Fig. 2.2, so that each scale of the one falls on one scale of the other. For instance, let the three variables in the given nomogram be denoted by U, V, and W, and let the U scale fall on the u scale of Fig. 2.2, the V scale on the v scale, and the W scale on the w scale. Then, for any value of U, we have a point of the U scale. This coincides with a point of the u scale and therefore corresponds to a value of u. Thus u may be regarded as a function of U, or *vice versa*. Similarly, v and V, and finally w and W, are functions of each other. We say that the given nomogram has been mapped on Fig. 2.2. Instead of Fig. 2.2, we may use Fig. 3.9 by identifying u with q_1, v with q_2, and w with a. Making use of the functional relationships just obtained, we mark the scale graduations for the U and V scales on the q scale and those for the W scale on the a scale. In general, even though the U and V scales are marked on the same curve, corresponding graduation marks do not coincide. In that case, it is usually convenient to have the graduation marks for one variable in the form of short dashes attached to the outside of the circle, and those for the other variable attached to the inside.

If the three straight-line scales of the given nomogram do not intersect in a single point, they will intersect in pairs in three points. One of these is projected to infinity, so that two of the scales become parallel. By other suitable transformations (shear, stretch, rotation, and translation), the nomogram is brought into coincidence with and mapped on Fig. 2.4. Finally, by comparison of Eqs. (2.21) and (2.33), we pass to the circular form as before. We shall return to this subject in Chapter VIII.

PROBLEM 3.18. Transform the nomogram represented by the following equation into a circular nomogram:

$$\begin{vmatrix} 1 + U^2 & 2U^2 & 1 \\ V & 2 + 3V & 1 \\ 3 + 4W & 5 - W & 1 \end{vmatrix} = 0. \tag{3.33}$$

PROBLEM 3.19. Transform the nomogram represented by the following equation into a circular nomogram:

$$\begin{vmatrix} 1 + U^2 & 2U^2 & 1 \\ \dfrac{31}{44}\dfrac{1}{V} & \dfrac{1}{V} & 1 \\ 3 + 4W & 5 - W & 1 \end{vmatrix} = 0. \tag{3.34}$$

PROBLEM 3.20. Let A, B, C be the angles of a spherical triangle and let a, b, c respectively be the sides opposite these angles. If $B = 90°$, it can be proved that $\tan C \sin a = \tan c$. Construct a circular nomogram for this equation if each of the quantities a, c, C may range from $0°$ to $180°$. Should the $\sin a$ of this problem be identified with q_1, q_2, $+b$, or $-b$ in Fig. 3.9? Why? If the values of a, c, and C had been allowed to range only from $0°$ to $90°$, could an N chart (or a projective transform thereof) have been constructed with the used portions of all three scales in a finite portion of the plane?

CHAPTER IV

Matrix Multiplication*

4.1. Fundamentals

Matrix addition is defined only when the two matrices to be added have the same number of rows and the same number of columns. The sum $[c] = [a] + [b]$ is defined in such a manner that $c_{ij} = a_{ij} + b_{ij}$, that is, each element of the sum is obtained by adding together those two elements of the summands which have the same row number and the same column number. It is easy to see that matrix addition obeys the associative and commutative laws.

The product of two matrices is defined only if the first has as many columns as the second has rows. The product

$$[c] = [a] \times [b] \tag{4.1}$$

is defined in such a manner that

$$c_{ij} = \sum_{r=1}^{n} a_{ir} b_{rj}, \tag{4.2}$$

where n is the number of columns in $[a]$ or the number of rows in $[b]$. In general, matrices do not obey the commutative law of multiplication. If an occasional pair of matrices do obey this law, they are said to commute. In the case of Eq.

* This chapter is more advanced and may be omitted without loss of continuity.

(4.1), we say that $[a]$ is post-multiplied by $[b]$, or that $[b]$ is pre-multiplied by $[a]$.

The definitions of matrix addition and multiplication are, of course, quite arbitrary. They were introduced into mathematics because they have practical applications, as we shall see presently.

Although matrix multiplication does not obey the commutative law in general, it does obey the associative law.

PROBLEM 4.1. The proof of this is left as an exercise for the reader.

Consider the system of linear equations

$$
\begin{aligned}
y_1 &= a_{11}x_1 + a_{12}x_2 + a_{13}x_3 + \ldots\ldots + a_{1n}x_n \\
y_2 &= a_{21}x_1 + a_{22}x_2 + a_{23}x_3 + \ldots\ldots + a_{2n}x_n \\
y_3 &= a_{31}x_1 + a_{32}x_2 + a_{33}x_3 + \ldots\ldots + a_{3n}x_n \quad (4.3) \\
&\ldots\ldots\ldots\ldots\ldots\ldots\ldots\ldots\ldots\ldots\ldots\ldots\ldots \\
&\ldots\ldots\ldots\ldots\ldots\ldots\ldots\ldots\ldots\ldots\ldots\ldots\ldots \\
y_n &= a_{n1}x_1 + a_{n2}x_2 + a_{n3}x_3 + \ldots\ldots + a_{nn}x_n
\end{aligned}
$$

This may be written in matrix notation thus

$$
\begin{bmatrix} y_1 \\ y_2 \\ y_3 \\ . \\ . \\ . \\ . \\ y_n \end{bmatrix} = \begin{bmatrix} a_{11} & a_{12} & a_{13}\ldots\ldots a_{1n} \\ a_{21} & a_{22} & a_{23}\ldots\ldots a_{2n} \\ a_{31} & a_{32} & a_{33}\ldots\ldots a_{3n} \\ \ldots\ldots\ldots\ldots\ldots\ldots \\ \ldots\ldots\ldots\ldots\ldots\ldots \\ \ldots\ldots\ldots\ldots\ldots\ldots \\ \ldots\ldots\ldots\ldots\ldots\ldots \\ a_{n1} & a_{n2} & a_{n3}\ldots\ldots a_{nn} \end{bmatrix} \times \begin{bmatrix} x_1 \\ x_2 \\ x_3 \\ . \\ . \\ . \\ . \\ x_n \end{bmatrix} \quad (4.4)
$$

as the reader may prove with the aid of Eq. (4.2). Likewise, the system of equations

$$
\begin{aligned}
z_1 &= b_{11}y_1 + b_{12}y_2 + b_{13}y_3 + \ldots\ldots + b_{1n}y_n \\
z_2 &= b_{21}y_1 + b_{22}y_2 + b_{23}y_3 + \ldots\ldots + b_{2n}y_n \\
z_3 &= b_{31}y_1 + b_{32}y_2 + b_{33}y_3 + \ldots\ldots + b_{3n}y_n \quad (4.5) \\
&\ldots\ldots\ldots\ldots\ldots\ldots\ldots\ldots\ldots\ldots\ldots\ldots\ldots \\
&\ldots\ldots\ldots\ldots\ldots\ldots\ldots\ldots\ldots\ldots\ldots\ldots\ldots \\
z_n &= b_{n1}y_1 + b_{n2}y_2 + b_{n3}y_3 + \ldots\ldots + b_{nn}y_n
\end{aligned}
$$

may be written

$$
\begin{bmatrix} z_1 \\ z_2 \\ z_3 \\ . \\ . \\ . \\ . \\ z_n \end{bmatrix} = \begin{bmatrix} b_{11} & b_{12} & b_{13} \ldots \ldots b_{1n} \\ b_{21} & b_{22} & b_{23} \ldots \ldots b_{2n} \\ b_{31} & b_{32} & b_{33} \ldots \ldots b_{3n} \\ \ldots \ldots \ldots \ldots \ldots \ldots \\ \ldots \ldots \ldots \ldots \ldots \ldots \\ \ldots \ldots \ldots \ldots \ldots \ldots \\ \ldots \ldots \ldots \ldots \ldots \ldots \\ b_{n1} & b_{n2} & b_{n3} \ldots \ldots b_{nn} \end{bmatrix} \times \begin{bmatrix} y_1 \\ y_2 \\ y_3 \\ . \\ . \\ . \\ . \\ y_n \end{bmatrix} \qquad (4.6)
$$

Substituting for the y's from Eqs. (4.3) into Eqs. (4.5), we obtain a result which may be written in matrix notation:

$$
\begin{bmatrix} z_1 \\ z_2 \\ z_3 \\ . \\ . \\ . \\ z_n \end{bmatrix} = \begin{bmatrix} b_{11} & b_{12} & b_{13} \ldots \ldots b_{1n} \\ b_{21} & b_{22} & b_{23} \ldots \ldots b_{2n} \\ b_{31} & b_{32} & b_{33} \ldots \ldots b_{3n} \\ \ldots \ldots \ldots \ldots \ldots \ldots \\ \ldots \ldots \ldots \ldots \ldots \ldots \\ \ldots \ldots \ldots \ldots \ldots \ldots \\ b_{n1} & b_{n2} & b_{n3} \ldots \ldots b_{nn} \end{bmatrix}
$$

$$
\times \begin{bmatrix} a_{11} & a_{12} & a_{13} \ldots \ldots a_{1n} \\ a_{21} & a_{22} & a_{23} \ldots \ldots a_{2n} \\ a_{31} & a_{32} & a_{33} \ldots \ldots a_{3n} \\ \ldots \ldots \ldots \ldots \ldots \ldots \\ \ldots \ldots \ldots \ldots \ldots \ldots \\ \ldots \ldots \ldots \ldots \ldots \ldots \\ a_{n1} & a_{n2} & a_{n3} \ldots \ldots a_{nn} \end{bmatrix} \times \begin{bmatrix} x_1 \\ x_2 \\ x_3 \\ . \\ . \\ . \\ x_n \end{bmatrix}. \qquad (4.7)
$$

PROBLEM 4.2. The proof is left as an exercise for the reader. In matrix notation, the proof amounts to a simple substitution of the expression for the matrix $[y]$ from Eq. (4.4) into Eq. (4.6).

4.2. Multiplication Theorem

We now come to a most important and fascinating theorem.

THEOREM 4.1. When two square matrices are multiplied together, the determinant of their product equals the product of their determinants. In symbols: If

$$[c] = [a] \times [b], \qquad (4.8)$$

then

$$|c| = |a| \times |b|. \qquad (4.9)$$

Proof: In $|c|$, we shall express the elements of the first column with the aid of Eq. (4.2). With the aid of Theorems 1.5 and 1.6, we obtain

$$|c| = \begin{vmatrix} a_{11}b_{11} + a_{12}b_{21} + \ldots\ldots + a_{1n}b_{n1} & c_{12} & c_{13}\ldots\ldots c_{1n} \\ a_{21}b_{11} + a_{22}b_{21} + \ldots\ldots + a_{2n}b_{n1} & c_{22} & c_{23}\ldots\ldots c_{2n} \\ \ldots\ldots\ldots\ldots\ldots\ldots\ldots\ldots\ldots & & \ldots\ldots\ldots\ldots \\ \ldots\ldots\ldots\ldots\ldots\ldots\ldots\ldots\ldots & & \ldots\ldots\ldots\ldots \\ a_{n1}b_{11} + a_{n2}b_{21} + \ldots\ldots + a_{nn}b_{n1} & c_{n2} & c_{n3}\ldots\ldots c_{nn} \end{vmatrix}$$

$$= \sum_{\alpha=1}^{n} b_{\alpha 1} \times \begin{vmatrix} a_{1\alpha} & c_{12} & c_{13}\ldots\ldots c_{1n} \\ a_{2\alpha} & c_{22} & c_{23}\ldots\ldots c_{2n} \\ \cdot & & \ldots\ldots\ldots\ldots \\ \cdot & & \ldots\ldots\ldots\ldots \\ \cdot & & \ldots\ldots\ldots\ldots \\ a_{n\alpha} & c_{n2} & c_{n3}\ldots\ldots c_{nn} \end{vmatrix}. \qquad (4.10)$$

Proceeding similarly with all the other columns, we obtain

$$|c| = \sum_{\alpha=1}^{n} \sum_{\beta=1}^{n} \ldots\ldots \sum_{\nu=1}^{n} b_{\alpha 1}b_{\beta 2}\ldots\ldots b_{\nu n} \begin{vmatrix} a_{1\alpha} & a_{1\beta} & \ldots\ldots a_{1\nu} \\ a_{2\alpha} & a_{2\beta} & \ldots\ldots a_{2\nu} \\ \ldots\ldots\ldots\ldots\ldots\ldots \\ \ldots\ldots\ldots\ldots\ldots\ldots \\ a_{n\alpha} & a_{n\beta}\ldots\ldots a_{n\nu} \end{vmatrix}. \qquad (4.11)$$

The multiple summation in the right-hand member of Eq. (4.11) has no fewer than n^n terms, each containing a determinant as a factor. Most of these terms are zero, namely all those for which any two or more of the subscripts α, β, $\ldots$, ν are equal, since then the determinant has two or more identical columns (Theorem 1.3). In the nonzero terms, the subscripts α, β, $\ldots$, ν are the integers 1, 2, 3, $\ldots$, n permuted in all possible ways. The determinant in each term is obtained from the determinant $|a|$ by permuting the n columns in any one of the $n!$ possible ways. It is therefore equal to $|a|$, except perhaps for the sign (Theorem 1.2). As for the product $b_{\alpha 1}b_{\beta 2}\ldots b_{\nu n}$, which also occurs as a factor in each term, it has the second subscripts in increasing order. The first subscripts are the same integers in some other order. In other words, the b's in this product are chosen from among the elements of the matrix $[b]$ in such a way that no two are taken from the same row or the same column. It is of such products that the expansion of the determinant $|b|$ is made up. It remains to be proved that the signs of these products in the expansion of $|b|$ agree with those of the nonzero terms in the right-hand member of Eq. (4.11).

In the course of the proof of Theorem 1.4, we showed that the rule of inversions which gives the signs of the terms in the expansion of a determinant may be applied to the first subscripts when the second subscripts are in increasing order (as they are in the product of b's in Eq. (4.11)). Now it will be seen that an interchange of two of the first subscripts will then require a change in the sign to be written in front of the term. For if the first subscripts to be interchanged are affixed to two neighboring b's, their interchange changes (that is increases or decreases) the number of inversions by one. And if they are not affixed to neighboring b's, their interchange is equivalent to an odd number of interchanges of first subscripts of neighboring b's. The reasoning used here is analogous to that used in the proof of Theorem 1.2.

In the right-hand member of Eq. (4.11), one of the nonzero terms is $+b_{11}b_{22}b_{33}\ldots\ldots b_{nn}|a|$. From this, we obtain all other nonzero terms by permuting the first subscripts of the b's in all possible ways and by permuting the columns of the determinant $|a|$ in the same manner in each term. Now, every permutation may be arrived at by successive interchanges of pairs of first subscripts of the b's and of the corresponding columns of the determinant $|a|$. Every such interchange changes the sign of the determinant $|a|$ and thereby provides the product of the b's with precisely that sign which will make it a term in the expansion of the determinant $|b|$. It follows that the right-hand member of Eq. (4.11) equals the product of the determinants $|a|$ and $|b|$, which was to be proved.

4.3. Generalized Projective Transformations

The transformations discussed in the preceding chapter, and any combination thereof, can be described in terms of matrix notation. This will be seen as follows. Let the nomogram be described by Eq. (2.7) or (2.8). In either case, the elements of each row depend on only one of the three variables. Let the matrix

$$\begin{bmatrix} y_u & x_u & 1 \\ y_v & x_v & 1 \\ y_w & x_w & 1 \end{bmatrix}$$

be denoted by $[N]$ and its determinant by $|N|$. Then Eq. (2.7) may be written $|N| = 0$. We shall introduce the transformation matrix

$$[k] = \begin{bmatrix} k_{11} & k_{12} & k_{13} \\ k_{21} & k_{22} & k_{23} \\ k_{31} & k_{32} & k_{33} \end{bmatrix}$$

whose elements are independent of u, v, and w and whose determinant $|k|$ is not equal to zero. Now let

$$[M] = [N] \times [k]. \tag{4.12}$$

Since $|N| = 0$, it follows from Theorem 4.1 that

$$|M| = |N| \times |k| = 0. \tag{4.13}$$

Writing out the elements of $[M]$ in terms of those of $[N]$ and $[k]$, we obtain

$$\begin{vmatrix} y_u k_{11} + x_u k_{21} + k_{31} & y_u k_{12} + x_u k_{22} + k_{32} & y_u k_{13} + x_u k_{23} + k_{33} \\ y_v k_{11} + x_v k_{21} + k_{31} & y_v k_{12} + x_v k_{22} + k_{32} & y_v k_{13} + x_v k_{23} + k_{33} \\ y_w k_{11} + x_w k_{21} + k_{31} & y_w k_{12} + x_w k_{22} + k_{32} & y_w k_{13} + x_w k_{23} + k_{33} \end{vmatrix} = 0.$$

$$\tag{4.14}$$

This is of the form of Eq. (2.8), since the first row of $[M]$ depends only on u, the second only on v, and the third only on w. Equation (4.14) may therefore be brought into the same form as Eq. (2.7), as described in Section 2.1. Assuming that the elements in the last column are nonzero, we divide each row by its element in the last column and obtain

$$\begin{vmatrix} \dfrac{y_u k_{11} + x_u k_{21} + k_{31}}{y_u k_{13} + x_u k_{23} + k_{33}} & \dfrac{y_u k_{12} + x_u k_{22} + k_{32}}{y_u k_{13} + x_u k_{23} + k_{33}} & 1 \\[2ex] \dfrac{y_v k_{11} + x_v k_{21} + k_{31}}{y_v k_{13} + x_v k_{23} + k_{33}} & \dfrac{y_v k_{12} + x_v k_{22} + k_{32}}{y_v k_{13} + x_v k_{23} + k_{33}} & 1 \\[2ex] \dfrac{y_w k_{11} + x_w k_{21} + k_{31}}{y_w k_{13} + x_w k_{23} + k_{33}} & \dfrac{y_w k_{12} + x_w k_{22} + k_{32}}{y_w k_{13} + x_w k_{23} + k_{33}} & 1 \end{vmatrix} = 0. \quad (4.15)$$

Note that all three rows of the determinant of Eq. (2.7) have been transformed according to the same law. In the longhand notation of Chapter III, this law of transformation may be written

$$y' = \frac{y k_{11} + x k_{21} + k_{31}}{y k_{13} + x k_{23} + k_{33}}, \quad (4.16)$$

$$x' = \frac{y k_{12} + x k_{22} + k_{32}}{y k_{13} + x k_{23} + k_{33}}. \quad (4.17)$$

It is immaterial for the validity of this argument whether we start with the matrix $[N]$, as we have done, or with

$$[P] = \begin{bmatrix} a_u & b_u & c_u \\ a_v & b_v & c_v \\ a_w & b_w & c_w \end{bmatrix} \quad (4.18)$$

(see Eq. (2.8)), of which $[N]$ is a special case. Omitting the subscripts, we have for any one row of $[P]$:

$$y = \frac{a}{c}, \quad x = \frac{b}{c}, \quad (4.19)$$

so that the effect of starting with $[P]$ would only be to multiply the numerators and denominators in the right-hand members of Eqs. (4.16) and (4.17) by c. Note that all the transformations discussed in Chapter III are of this form. For instance, comparing Eqs. (4.16) and (4.17) to Eqs. (3.3) and (3.4), we find for rotation of coordinates:

$$k_{11} = \cos \theta, \qquad k_{21} = \sin \theta, \qquad k_{31} = k_{13} = k_{23} = k_{32} = 0,$$

$$k_{12} = -\sin \theta, \qquad k_{22} = \cos \theta, \qquad k_{33} = 1.$$

Or, in matrix notation, the transformation matrix for rotation of coordinates is

$$[k_{\text{rot}}] = \begin{bmatrix} +\cos \theta & -\sin \theta & 0 \\ +\sin \theta & +\cos \theta & 0 \\ 0 & 0 & 1 \end{bmatrix}. \qquad (4.20)$$

Similarly, for a projective transformation, we obtain from Eqs. (3.13) and (3.14) the transformation matrix

$$[k_{\text{proj}}] = \begin{bmatrix} -\bar{x} & 0 & 0 \\ +\bar{y} & +\bar{z} & 1 \\ 0 & 0 & -\bar{x} \end{bmatrix}. \qquad (4.21)$$

PROBLEM 4.3. As exercises the reader may derive the transformation matrices for translation, stretch, and shear.

The transformation described by Eqs. (4.16) and (4.17) is concisely represented by the transformation matrix $[k]$. If several such transformations are to be performed in succession, they may be combined into one by the simple expedient of multiplying the individual transformation matrices together in the order in which the transformations are to be performed. This follows at once from the associative law of matrix multiplication.

4.4. Transformation of an Arbitrary Quadrilateral into a Rectangle

Since the methods of the preceding and the present chapter accomplish the same result, the choice between them is largely a matter of personal preference. On the one hand, many transformations which are frequently used must be broken down into several successive steps when performed by the methods of Chapter III, whereas the present method would enable us to obtain the required transformation matrix to perform the transformation in one step.   On the other hand, the methods of Chapter III permit easy visualization, so that errors are easier to avoid or detect.   For instance, suppose we wish to transform the quadrilateral

$$(x_1, y_1), \quad (x_2, y_2), \quad (x_3, y_3), \quad (x_4, y_4)$$

into the rectangle

$$(0, 0), \quad (0, a), \quad (b, 0), \quad (b, a).$$

Substituting into Eqs. (4.16) and (4.17), we obtain

$$0 = y_1 k_{11} + x_1 k_{21} + k_{31} \tag{4.22a}$$

$$0 = y_1 k_{12} + x_1 k_{22} + k_{32} \tag{4.22b}$$

$$0 = y_2 k_{12} + x_2 k_{22} + k_{32} \tag{4.22c}$$

$$a = \frac{y_2 k_{11} + x_2 k_{21} + k_{31}}{y_2 k_{13} + x_2 k_{23} + k_{33}} \tag{4.22d}$$

$$b = \frac{y_3 k_{12} + x_3 k_{22} + k_{32}}{y_3 k_{13} + x_3 k_{23} + k_{33}} \tag{4.22e}$$

$$0 = y_3 k_{11} + x_3 k_{21} + k_{31} \tag{4.22f}$$

$$b = \frac{y_4 k_{12} + x_4 k_{22} + k_{32}}{y_4 k_{13} + x_4 k_{23} + k_{33}} \tag{4.22g}$$

$$a = \frac{y_4 k_{11} + x_4 k_{21} + k_{31}}{y_4 k_{13} + x_4 k_{23} + k_{33}}. \tag{4.22h}$$

We have here eight equations in nine unknowns, the k's.   One of the k's may be chosen arbitrarily, and the equations may then be solved for the others.   The reader may try Problem 3.7 by this method.   For comparison, the matrices for the rotation, projection, the second rotation, and the final shear used there may be written out and multiplied together.   The elements of the resulting matrix product should satisfy the above Eqs. (4.22) for the k's.

4.5. *Transformation of the Circular Nomogram to the Standard Form*

As a final example, consider the transformation of Eq. (2.29) into Eq. (3.31). The q scale in Eq. (2.29) is a hyperbola. If any straight line which does not intersect either branch of the hyperbola is projected to infinity, the hyperbola transforms into an ellipse. An infinite number of such transformations are possible. From among these, we arbitrarily select one which projects the straight line

$$y + x - 1 = 0 \tag{4.23}$$

to infinity.

PROBLEM 4.4. The proof that this line does not intersect the q scale of Eq. (2.29) is left as an exercise for the reader.

From Eqs. (4.16) and (4.17) it will be seen that the line

$$yk_{13} + xk_{23} + k_{33} = 0 \tag{4.24}$$

is projected to infinity. Comparing Eqs. (4.23) and (4.24), we obtain

$$k_{13} = k_{23} = 1, \quad k_{33} = -1. \tag{4.25}$$

After transformation, we want the a scale to fall along the x' axis and the b scale along the y' axis, with the points $a = \infty$ and $b = \infty$ at the origin. From Eq. (2.29), we have:

$$y_a = a, \quad x_a = 1, \tag{4.26}$$

$$y_b = b, \quad x_b = 0. \tag{4.27}$$

It is now desired that

$$y_a' = 0, \tag{4.28}$$

$$x_b' = 0, \tag{4.29}$$

$$x_a' = 0 \quad \text{when } a = \infty, \tag{4.30}$$

$$y_b' = 0 \quad \text{when } b = \infty, \tag{4.31}$$

$$y_b' = 1 \quad \text{when } b = 0, \tag{4.32}$$

$$x_{q \, max} = {}^1\!/_2. \tag{4.33}$$

From Eqs. (4.25), (4.16), and (4.17):

$$y' = \frac{yk_{11} + xk_{21} + k_{31}}{y + x - 1}, \tag{4.34}$$

$$x' = \frac{yk_{12} + xk_{22} + k_{32}}{y + x - 1}. \tag{4.35}$$

From (4.26), (4.28), and (4.34):

$$0 = ak_{11} + k_{21} + k_{31}. \tag{4.36}$$

From (4.27), (4.29), and (4.35):

$$0 = bk_{12} + k_{32}. \tag{4.37}$$

From (4.26) and (4.35):

$$x_a' = \frac{ak_{12} + k_{22} + k_{32}}{a}. \tag{4.38}$$

Hence, by (4.30):

$$\lim_{a \to \infty} x_a' = k_{12} = 0. \tag{4.39}$$

From (4.27) and (4.34):

$$y_b' = \frac{bk_{11} + k_{31}}{b - 1}. \tag{4.40}$$

From this and (4.31):

$$\lim_{b \to \infty} y_b' = k_{11} = 0. \tag{4.41}$$

From (4.32) and (4.40):

$$+1 = -k_{31}. \tag{4.42}$$

Solving Eqs. (4.36), (4.37), (4.39), (4.41), and (4.42) for the k's contained in them, we obtain:

$$k_{11} = k_{12} = k_{32} = 0, \tag{4.43}$$

$$k_{31} = -1, \tag{4.44}$$

$$k_{21} = +1. \tag{4.45}$$

Together with Eqs. (4.25), these give eight of the nine elements of the transformation matrix k. To obtain the remaining element, we gather from Eq. (2.29):

$$y_q = \frac{q^2}{q - 1}, \qquad x_q = \frac{q}{q - 1}. \qquad (4.46)$$

Substituting these into (4.17) and making use of the k's already obtained, we have:

$$x_q' = \frac{qk_{22}}{q^2 + q - q + 1} = \frac{qk_{22}}{q^2 + 1}. \qquad (4.47)$$

For locating the maximum of x_q' as a function of q, a knowledge of calculus is required. Lacking this, the reader may locate the maximum approximately by trial and error or graphically. It occurs when $q = +1$, and its value is

$$x_q'{}_{\max} = {}^1/_2 k_{22}. \qquad (4.48)$$

Hence, from Eq. (4.33):

$$k_{22} = 1. \qquad (4.49)$$

The transformation matrix is therefore

$$[k] = \begin{bmatrix} 0 & 0 & 1 \\ 1 & 1 & 1 \\ -1 & 0 & -1 \end{bmatrix}. \qquad (4.50)$$

Applying this to Eq. (2.29) and reducing the result to the standard form, we obtain at once Eq. (3.31).

CHAPTER V

More Than Three Variables

5.1. *Grid Nomograms*

Some fairly obvious devices suggest themselves for the nomographic representation of equations involving more than three variables. For instance, if an equation involving four variables u, v, w, q is to be nomographed, w may be treated as a parameter, and a separate scale for q may be constructed for every value of w. Thus, a single scale is replaced with a family of scales which form a grid. Hence the name grid nomogram for this type of chart.

As an example, consider the cubic equation

$$q^3 + uq^2 + vq + w = 0, \tag{5.1}$$

where q is the unknown, and u, v, and w are given constants. This may be written in the form

$$(q^3 + w) + uq^2 + vq = 0 \tag{5.2}$$

and may then be rewritten in determinant notation:

$$\begin{vmatrix} q^3 + w & q^2 & -q \\ -u & 1 & 0 \\ v & 0 & 1 \end{vmatrix} = 0. \tag{5.3}$$

Here, one row depends on two variables, the others on one variable each. Equation (5.3) may be reduced to the standard form (2.7) as explained in Section 2.1 and may then be nomographed.

61

PROBLEM 5.1. The details are left as an exercise for the reader.

The result may or may not be of value. If some of the scales forming the grid intersect, the resulting tangle of scales may be difficult to read.

PROBLEM 5.2. In the case of Eq. (5.1), we have used single scales for u and v and a grid for q and w. Alternatively, we could have combined q and u or q and v to form a grid. These two possibilities are left as exercises for the reader.

An equation involving at most six variables may be capable of representation by a grid nomogram. In this case, we must try to write the equation as a determinant equated to zero, where each row depends on at most two variables, and no variable occurs in more than one row.

5.2. Multiple Alignment Charts

It is frequently possible to replace an equation in four variables with two equations in three variables each, through the introduction of an auxiliary variable. For instance, suppose we wish to nomograph the equation

$$q = uvw. \tag{5.4}$$

In this case, let

$$r = uv. \tag{5.5}$$

Then

$$q = rw. \tag{5.6}$$

Through the introduction of the auxiliary variable r, we have replaced Eq. (5.4) with Eqs. (5.5) and (5.6). In this case, each of Eqs. (5.5) and (5.6) can be nomographed. Furthermore, this can be done in such a manner that the same r scale is used for both nomograms. If the value of r is not of interest for its own sake, the r scale need not even be graduated. Just the smooth curve (in this case a straight line) is all that is required. Either the form Fig. 2.3 or Fig. 2.4 may be used.

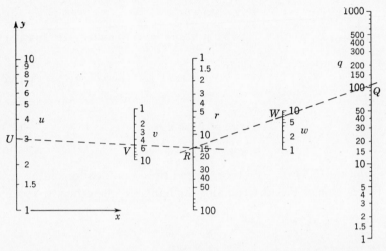

Figure 5.1

Figures 5.1 and 5.2 show nomograms based on these two types. Their use is straightforward. Given u and v, we find the corresponding points U and V on their respective scales and draw a straight line through them, which intersects the r scale in a point R. (An example is drawn in Fig. 5.1 for $u = 3$, $v = 5$, $w = 7$.) Through this point and the point W corresponding to the desired value of w, another straight line is drawn to its intersection Q with the q scale, where the answer may be read.

In effect, we have represented an equation in four variables by a combination of two nomograms, and the straight edge has to be positioned twice. In general, if an equation in n variables is to be nomographed, we try to represent it by a combination of $n - 2$ nomograms. This may not always be possible. Such combinations of nomograms are called multiple alignment charts.

5.3. Discussion

The choice between nomograms of the types represented by Figs. 2.3 and 2.4 is not always immaterial. Consider the equation

$$q = u^v w. \tag{5.7}$$

This may be written as two equations with the aid of the auxiliary variable

$$r = u^v \tag{5.8}$$

thus:

$$\log r = v \log u \tag{5.9}$$

$$\log q = \log r + \log w. \tag{5.10}$$

Equation (5.9) may be represented by a modification of Fig. 2.4. The v scale of Fig. 2.4 remains unchanged; the other two scales

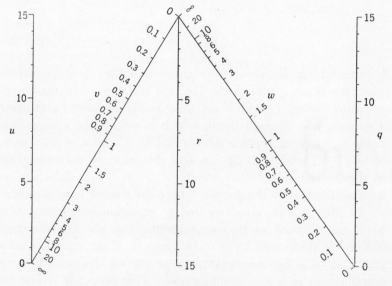

Figure 5.2

are replaced with logarithmic scales. Equation (5.10) is represented by Fig. 2.3. (The relabeling of the scales should be obvious.) The r scale is then shared by the two nomograms.

As another example, consider the equation

$$q = (u + v)w. \tag{5.11}$$

This time, we define the auxiliary variable to be

$$r = u + v \tag{5.12}$$

so that

$$q = rw. \tag{5.13}$$

Equation (5.12) may be conveniently represented by a nomogram of the type of Fig. 2.2. Equation (5.13) may then be represented by the type of Fig. 2.4, the r scale being shared by the two nomograms. Here, as in the preceding example, it is unnecessary to graduate the r scale unless the value of r is of interest for its own sake.

In Section 3.3, we pointed out that, in a nomogram relating three variables, it is most advantageous to place the answer scale between the two data scales. A multiple alignment nomogram relating four variables is essentially a combination of two nomograms in three variables each, the answer scale of the first being one of the data scales of the second. In this case, it is usually advantageous to make the order of scales in each three-scale nomogram datum-datum-answer (as was done in Figs. 5.1 and 5.2), even though this means that the second datum scale is shorter than the others. If the answer scale of each three-scale nomogram were placed between the two data scales, the result would be an interlacing of the scales of the two partial nomograms, and this would be confusing. The reader should construct his own figures corresponding to 5.1 and 5.2 to illustrate these arguments. The generalization of these arguments to multiple alignment nomograms relating more than four variables should be obvious.

PROBLEM 5.3. Nomograph Eqs. (5.7) and (5.11) and the equation $q = uv + w$, using the two alternative sequences of scales discussed in the text. Let each datum range from 1 to 10. If the w scale of Fig. 2.4 becomes graduated at unequal intervals as the result of a rearrangement, how would you treat the next three-scale nomogram to permit use of the same intermediate scale by both three-scale nomograms?

Sometimes, it is impossible to design a multiple alignment chart such that the answer scale of each component three-scale nomogram can serve identically as the data scale of the next. For instance, let

$$q = u^v + w. \tag{5.14}$$

If we write

$$r = u^v, \tag{5.15}$$

we must represent r by a logarithmic scale in the first three-scale nomogram and by a linear scale in the second. In this case, we connect corresponding graduation marks of the two scales with guide lines, as shown in Fig. 5.3. The resulting

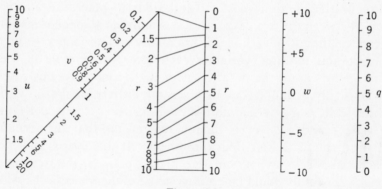

Figure 5.3

double scale is called a ladder scale. It is admittedly a crutch but is widely used.

PROBLEM 5.4. Subject either of the two three-scale nomograms which together constitute Fig. 5.3 to a projective transformation in an attempt to make the "rungs" of the ladder scale more nearly horizontal and parallel.

5.4. High-Accuracy Nomograms

The accuracy of a nomogram is never good, and this is generally true of graphical processes. Moreover it decreases as the number of variables of a multiple alignment chart increases. For instance, consider a multiple alignment chart giving the sum of n quantities any one of which can range from 0 to 10. Then the sum can range from 0 to $10n$. If all scales are equally long, the error in reading the answer scale is likely to be n times as large as the error in reading any one of the data scales.

For the special case of a nomogram consisting of three parallel (or concurrent) straight lines, L. R. Ford has given a modification which greatly improves the accuracy. We shall describe this as a modification of Fig. 2.3, although the same device is equally applicable to Fig. 2.2. Figure 2.3 is described by the equation

$$\begin{vmatrix} \log_{10} u & 0 & 1 \\ \log_{10} v & 1 & 1 \\ \dfrac{1}{2} \log_{10} w & \dfrac{1}{2} & 1 \end{vmatrix} = 0. \tag{5.16}$$

Ford's modification is a multiple nomogram described by

$$\begin{vmatrix} \log_{10} u - mb & -1 + 2ma & 1 \\ \log_{10} v - nb & +1 + 2na & 1 \\ \dfrac{1}{2} [\log_{10} w - (m+n)b] & (m+n)a & 1 \end{vmatrix} = 0, \tag{5.17}$$

where a and b are constants and m and n are integers. Figure 5.4 shows an example with $a = 0.05$, $b = 0.17$, and the resulting nomogram stretched in the y direction by a factor of 10. The parameters m, n, and $m + n$ are marked at the bottom of the scales. From these, the particular w scale to be used with any given u and v scales is easily identified. Projective transformations of this nomogram should not present any new problems.

Since Fig. 5.4 is intended for purposes of illustration only, the graduations of the sales have been made fairly coarse. With finer graduations, a very high accuracy would have been possible.

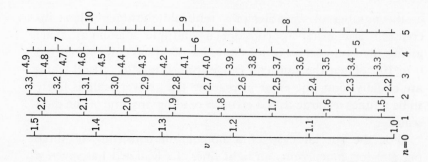

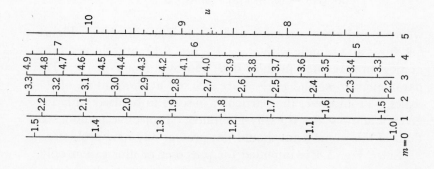

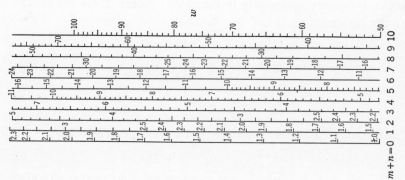

Figure 5.4

Ford points out that it would be very desirable if this device could be generalized to other types of nomograms. To the author's knowledge, this has never been accomplished.

The combination of nomograms of the type of Fig. 5.4 into multiple alignment charts appears attractive to counteract the otherwise inevitable decrease in accuracy as the number of variables increases. However, it is subject to severe limitations. It is applicable to a nomogram for the equation $q = uvwrst$, but not to $q = uv + w$. Even in the former case, there will be difficulties. If the scales for u and v each have two branches (that is, m and n can each take on the values 0 and 1), the scale for the intermediate product uv will have three branches. If then w is represented by a scale of two branches, uvw will be represented by a scale of four branches, and so on. The large number of branches may eventually become objectionable. In any case, the constants a and b should be chosen with care, or the branches of two different scales are liable to interlace or even coincide. Whether this would be objectionable is perhaps a matter of opinion.

5.5. Set-Square Nomogram

In the special case of a multiple alignment chart relating four variables where the intermediate answer scale is a straight line, we may project this intermediate scale to infinity. For instance, the two three-scale nomograms which make up Fig. 5.1 are described by the equations

$$\begin{vmatrix} \log u & 0 & 1 \\ \dfrac{2}{3} - \dfrac{1}{3}\log v & \dfrac{2}{3} & 1 \\ 1 - \dfrac{1}{2}\log r & 1 & 1 \end{vmatrix} = 0 \qquad (5.18)$$

and

$$\begin{vmatrix} 1 - \dfrac{1}{2}\log r & 1 & 1 \\[2mm] \dfrac{2}{5} + \dfrac{1}{4}\log w & \dfrac{3}{2} & 1 \\[2mm] -\dfrac{1}{5} + \dfrac{1}{2}\log q & 2 & 1 \end{vmatrix} = 0. \qquad (5.19)$$

These are subjected to the transformation of Eqs. (3.13) and (3.14) with $\bar{x} = 1$, $\bar{y} = {}^1\!/_2$, $\bar{z} = 1$. The results are

$$\begin{vmatrix} \log u & 0 & 1 \\ 1 - \log v & -2 & 1 \\ \infty & \infty & 1 \end{vmatrix} = 0 \qquad (5.20)$$

and

$$\begin{vmatrix} \infty & \infty & 1 \\[2mm] \dfrac{7}{10} - \dfrac{1}{2}\log w & 3 & 1 \\[2mm] \dfrac{6}{5} - \dfrac{1}{2}\log q & 2 & 1 \end{vmatrix} = 0. \qquad (5.21)$$

These are plotted in Fig. 5.5 The dotted lines are positions of the straight-edge used for reading the nomogram and illustrate the case $u = 3$, $v = 5$, $w = 7$. Since these two dotted lines intersect in a point at infinity, they are parallel. Now let one of the two three-scale nomograms forming Fig. 5.5 be rotated through 90° with respect to the other. Only two of the three scales are in sight, since the third (the intermediate scale) is at infinity. The straight line used for reading the nomogram rotates along with these two scales, so that the two dotted lines become mutually perpendicular, as shown in Fig. 5.6 for the same example. A translation of either three-scale nomogram parallel to itself is permitted and will not affect the validity of the construction. The same is true of a stretch by the same factor in both the x and y directions, although not of a stretch in either of these directions alone. Figure 5.6 may be read with the aid of a set square and is therefore called a set-square nomo-

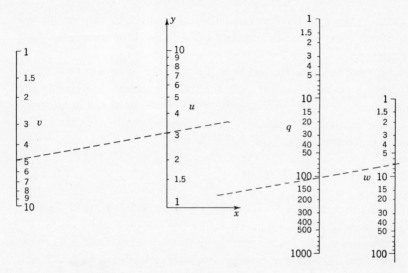

Figure 5.5

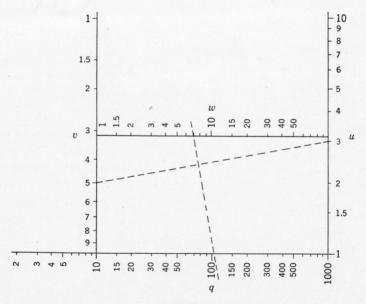

Figure 5.6

gram. More conveniently, it may be read with the aid of two mutually perpendicular straight lines drawn on a sheet of tracing paper.

Figure 5.5 is included here for the sake of explanation only. In practice, when only a set-square nomogram is desired, the intermediate stage corresponding to Fig. 5.5 need not be plotted.

PROBLEM 5.5. Construct a multiple alignment chart and a set-square nomogram for the following:

$$P = \frac{\cos \theta}{R^2 \, e^{\alpha R}}.$$

Let R range from 1 to 10, α from 0 to 1, and θ from $0°$ to $80°$. Take $e = 2.718$.

PROBLEM 5.6. In the transformation of a multiple alignment chart into a set-square nomogram, what variables can be chosen at pleasure to give scales of reasonable length in convenient positions?

CHAPTER VI

Empirical Nomography

6.1. Duality

Projective geometry deals with those properties of geometrical figures in a plane which remain unchanged by a projective transformation. For instance, if three or more straight lines intersect in a point (they are then said to be *concurrent*), they will retain this property after a projective transformation. For a thorough treatment of projective geometry, the reader must be referred to specialized textbooks. We attempted a brief outline of the subject by analytical methods in Chapter III. Historically, the first treatment of it used synthetic methods, much like Euclidean geometry, all theorems being derived from a set of axioms. It is a curious property of these axioms and of all theorems derivable from them that they can be arranged in pairs of duals, each axiom or theorem being obtained from its dual by an interchange of the terms *point* and *straight line*. As an example, compare the following two axioms:

(A) Two noncoincident straight lines in the same plane intersect in one and only one point (which may lie at infinity).

(B) Given any two noncoincident points, there exists one and only one straight line which passes through both.

These two statements are duals of each other. However, the duality is not at once apparent, since an interchange of the terms *point* and *straight line* in (A) does not yield (B), and *vice versa*. The difficulty lies with the English language, since it

73

is not customary to say that two points intersect in a straight line or that a point passes through a straight line. We can remedy this situation by taking some liberties with the English language. Thus, in place of (A), we shall write:

Two noncoincident straight lines in the same plane lie on one and only one point.

And in place of (B) we shall write:

Two noncoincident points in the same plane lie on one and only one straight line.

This terminology is widely used in textbooks of projective geometry.

We shall give an analytical method for obtaining a dual of any point or straight line, and we shall show that any figure so obtained has the desired properties. Let x, y be the cartesian coordinates in one plane, and ξ, η those in another plane. Now consider the equation

$$x\xi + y\eta = 1. \tag{6.1}$$

If ξ and η are given constants, they are the coordinates of a point in the $\xi\eta$ plane. Alternatively, Eq. (6.1) is then the equation of a straight line in the xy plane. We shall show presently that this point and this straight line are duals of each other. Note that $1/\xi$ is the x intercept of the straight line described by Eq. (6.1), and $1/\eta$ is its y intercept. In other words, the dual of a straight line is a point whose coordinates are the reciprocals of the x and y intercepts of the straight line, and conversely. Of course, the dual of any given figure is not unique, since it may be transformed by projection without losing the property of duality. In view of the symmetry of Eq. (6.1), it also furnishes the reverse construction, since constant values of x and y are the coordinates of a point in the xy plane, and Eq. (6.1) is then the equation of a straight line in the $\xi\eta$ plane.

To prove that the construction based on Eq. (6.1) yields a dual of any given figure, we must prove that the duals of any three collinear points as defined by Eq. (6.1) are three concurrent

straight lines, and conversely.   Let (x_u, y_u), (x_v, y_v), (x_w, y_w) be
the three given points in the xy plane.   The condition of collinearity of these three points is Eq. (2.7).   Substituting the
coordinates of these points in turn into Eq. (6.1) and rearranging
slightly, we obtain the equations

$$x_u\xi + y_u\eta - 1 = 0 \tag{6.2}$$

$$x_v\xi + y_v\eta - 1 = 0 \tag{6.3}$$

$$x_w\xi + y_w\eta - 1 = 0 \tag{6.4}$$

which describe three straight lines in the $\xi\eta$ plane.   These
straight lines will be concurrent if their equations are compatible, and, according to Theorem 1.9, the necessary and
sufficient condition for this is

$$\begin{vmatrix} x_u & y_u & -1 \\ x_v & y_v & -1 \\ x_w & y_w & -1 \end{vmatrix} = 0, \tag{6.5}$$

which yields Eq. (2.7) if the first two columns are interchanged
and the signs in the third column are changed.   Since Eq. (2.7)
is at the same time the condition for collinearity of three points
in the xy plane and the condition for concurrence of three
straight lines in the $\xi\eta$ plane, the property of duality follows.
The proof of the converse is immediate, since it is only necessary
to interchange x with ξ and y with η.

PROBLEM 6.1.   We have shown that the duals of three
collinear points as defined by Eq. (6.1) are three concurrent
straight lines.   Using this result, or otherwise, prove the corresponding proposition for more than three collinear points.

PROBLEM 6.2.   The coordinates x, y of a point in the xy plane
are the reciprocals of the ξ and η intercepts of the dual.   Accordingly, the ξ and η axes may be provided with scales to read
directly the x and y coordinates of the dual when a straight line
in the $\xi\eta$ plane is given.   Let the $\xi\eta$ plane be subjected to a
projective transformation such that the origin is projected to

infinity. What form will the x and y scales attached to the ξ and η axes take as a result of this transformation? The resulting scales were proposed by d'Ocagne for the construction of the dual of any given point.

Starting from Eq. (6.1) and passing to the limit as $x \to 0$, $y \to 0$, $\xi \to \infty$, and $\eta \to \infty$, we see that the dual of the origin is the line at infinity. Hence the dual of a line through the origin is a point at infinity. In Eq. (6.1), let the ratio ξ/η be prescribed, and let $\xi \to \infty$ and $\eta \to \infty$ in such a manner that ξ/η remains constant. Then, in the limit, the straight line in the xy plane approaches a straight line through the origin, whose slope is $-\xi/\eta$. The dual of this line is a point at infinity in the $\xi\eta$ plane. A family of parallel straight lines with slope equal to minus the reciprocal of the slope of the straight line in the xy plane intersect in this point.

6.2. Adams' Scanner

An ingenious device called a scanner has been proposed by D. P. Adams for the graphical construction of a dual of any given arrangement of straight lines. It consists of an accurately rectangular plate called a slider, to which is attached a circular disk (Fig. 6.1). Both the slider and the disk are made of transparent plastic. The disk is free to rotate about its center, where it is attached to the slider. Engraved on the disk are two mutually perpendicular straight lines l and m through its center. Engraved on the slider are two straight lines a and d. Line d passes through the center of rotation C of the disk and is parallel to one pair of edges of the slider, and line a is parallel to the other pair of edges. C is on one of these two edges, and the opposite edge is denoted by b.

We shall use rectangular coordinates ξ, η to describe the given diagram, and rectangular coordinates x', y' to describe the dual constructed with the aid of the scanner. A straight edge is fixed along the ξ axis. An edge of the slider parallel to d is brought into contact with this straight edge, so that the slider can slide along the ξ axis. Now let l be brought into

coincidence with the straight line whose dual is to be constructed.
Then m intersects a in a point Q.   Let a straight line QP be
drawn parallel to d to its intersection P with the edge b.   Then
P is the desired dual of l.   Two identical scales engraved on
a and b enable the user to locate P without drawing the line QP.

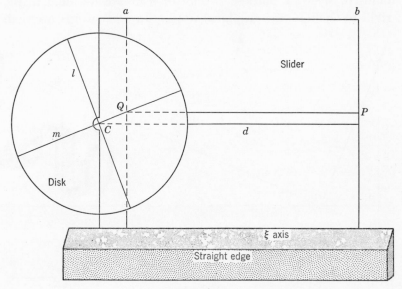

Figure 6.1

The dual of every straight line in the figure is constructed
in this manner.   If the given figure contains an occasional
isolated point, its dual is obtained as follows.   Two straight
lines are drawn through the given point, their duals are obtained,
and a straight line is drawn through the duals.   This straight
line is the dual of the given point.

This method fails only when the given straight line is parallel
or nearly parallel to the ξ axis, since then the line m will intersect
the line a outside the slider.   In practice, we can usually make
sure that no straight line of the given figure has this undesirable
orientation, simply by rotating the figure with respect to the
ξ axis (that is the straight edge).

It remains to be proved that the dual obtained by this construction is a projective transform of the dual defined by Eq. (6.1). Let the x' and y' axes coincide respectively with the ξ and η axes. Figure 6.2 shows (not to scale) the lines l, m, a, and d together with the ξ and η axes. The line b has been omitted, since its purpose is only to translate the dual to the right to facilitate the graphical work. In other words, we shall

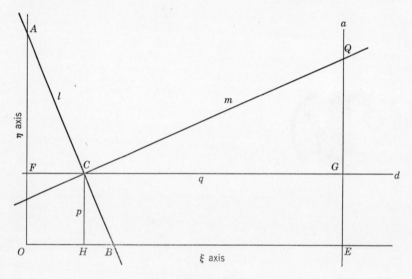

Figure 6.2

regard Q rather than P as the dual of l. The line d intersects a in G and the η axis in F. Line l intersects the η axis in A and the ξ axis in B. Line m intersects a in Q. The point H is the projection of C upon the ξ axis. The lengths $EG = FO = CH = p$ and $CG = q$ are constants characteristic of the scanner. O is the origin of coordinates.

Since l is the line whose dual is sought, we have from Section 6.1:

$$OB = \frac{1}{x}, \tag{6.6}$$

$$OA = \frac{1}{y}. \tag{6.7}$$

The coordinates of the point Q are

$$x' = FG = FC + CG \tag{6.8}$$

and

$$y' = EQ = EG + GQ. \tag{6.9}$$

The triangles AOB, AFC, and CGQ are similar.

PROBLEM 6.3. Prove triangles AOB, AFC, and CGQ are similar.

Since these triangles are similar,

$$\frac{OB}{OA} = \frac{FC}{FA} = \frac{GQ}{GC}. \tag{6.10}$$

Or, substituting the values where known, we obtain from (6.8) through (6.10):

$$x' = FC + q \tag{6.11}$$

$$y' = p + GQ \tag{6.12}$$

$$\frac{y}{x} = \frac{FC}{\frac{1}{y} - p} = \frac{GQ}{q}. \tag{6.13}$$

Eliminating FC and GQ between these, we obtain

$$x' = \frac{-yp + xq + 1}{x} \tag{6.14}$$

$$y' = \frac{yq + xp}{x}. \tag{6.15}$$

It remains to be proved that Eqs. (6.14) and (6.15) represent a projective transformation. This can be proved by the methods of either Chapter III or Chapter IV. The former proof is by far the more difficult but will be given first for the benefit of those readers who have not studied Chapter IV. We apply the following transformations in order. Use Eqs. (3.1) and (3.2) with $a = 1$ and $b = 0$. Use Eqs. (3.13) and (3.14) with $\bar{x} = 1, \bar{y} = 0, \bar{z} = 1/(p\sqrt{2})$. Perform the transformation

$$x' = x + \frac{y}{\sqrt{2}}, \tag{6.16}$$

$$y' = \frac{y}{\sqrt{2}}. \tag{6.17}$$

This is the shear illustrated in Fig. 6.3, where the x axis remains in the same position but the y axis is rotated through an angle

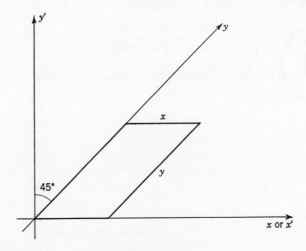

Figure 6.3

of 45°. It is analogous to the transformation of Fig. 3.3 and Eqs. (3.7) and (3.8), but with the roles of the x and y axes interchanged. Next, stretch the figure in the x direction by a factor of $p\sqrt{2}$, and in the y direction by a factor of $-q\sqrt{2}$. Finally, use Eqs. (3.1) and (3.2) with $a = q - 1$ and $b = +p$. Here as always when a number of transformations are to be applied in succession, double, triple, etc. primes may be used to distinguish the intermediate transforms.

PROBLEM 6.4. The details of the proof are left as an exercise for the reader.

To prove the same proposition by the method of Chapter IV, we need only compare Eqs. (6.14) and (6.15) to Eqs. (4.16) and (4.17) and identify the elements of the transformation matrix. Thus the proof becomes immediate.

6.3. Anamorphosis

A conventional nomogram or alignment chart consists of scales each of which is a continuum of points. Three values of the respective variables which are related in the prescribed manner correspond to three collinear scale points. Given any nomogram, we can construct its dual. In the latter, each scale is a family of straight lines. Three values of the respective variables which are related in the prescribed manner correspond to three concurrent straight lines. For this reason, the dual of an alignment chart is called an intersection chart. Given an intersection chart for any given equation, we can construct an alignment chart for the same equation by dualization.

An equation which is to be nomographed may first be solved for one of the variables:

$$w = w(u, v). \tag{6.18}$$

We may then graph w against u in cartesian coordinates, treating v as a parameter. In other words, we use a coordinate grid where the loci $u =$ constant and $w =$ constant are straight lines. If, in addition, the loci $v =$ constant are also straight lines, the resulting intersection diagram may be transformed into an alignment chart by dualization. However, more often, it will be found that the loci $v =$ constant are curved.

We now seek a transformation which has the following properties:

(A) A point transforms into a point.

(B) Any one of the straight lines $u =$ constant or $w =$ constant transforms into a straight line, while, in general, any other straight line does not necessarily transform into a straight line. Such a transformation is called an anamorphosis.

We now seek an anamorphosis such that the family of curves $v = $ constant transforms into a family of straight lines. From the transform, an alignment chart can be obtained by dualization. The method for obtaining the desired anamorphosis which we shall describe is graphical and approximate. It is primarily of value for nomographing empirical data which have not been put into the form of an equation. It can also be used for obtaining an approximate nomogram over a sufficiently narrow range of the variables for an equation which cannot be nomographed rigorously.

The problem of obtaining the desired anamorphosis has not been solved in general, but only in the case where

$$\xi = \xi(u) \tag{6.19}$$

$$\eta = \eta(w), \tag{6.20}$$

that is, the new cartesian coordinates ξ and η are functions of u and w respectively. Isolated instances may arise where Eq. (6.20) takes the form

$$\eta = w, \tag{6.21}$$

so that only the function $\xi(u)$ remains to be determined. By a suitable choice of this function, one curve of the family $v = $ constant can always be transformed into a straight line, and it may sometimes transform the other curves of the family into sufficiently close approximations to straight lines. This method is straightforward.

PROBLEM 6.5. The details of this method are left as an exercise for the reader.

Next, we shall describe an anamorphosis which transforms any two curves of the family $v = $ constant into straight lines. If these are chosen sufficiently close together, all curves of the family not too distant from these two will transform approximately into straight lines, and the approximation obtained is usually much closer than with the restriction of Eq. (6.21).

The following method of construction is due to A. Lafay. Consider first the following case. The two curves v = constant which are to be transformed into straight lines intersect once within the region of interest. (If they intersect more than once, the method breaks down.) Neither w as a function of u, nor u as a function of w, may have a maximum or minimum within the region of interest for any constant value of v. Let $v = v_1$ and $v = v_2$ be the two curves to be transformed into straight lines (Fig. 6.4), and let A_0 be their point of intersection. Primed symbols are generally used to denote corresponding points in the transform. The transforms of the two curves are two straight lines whose slopes are respectively equal to the slopes of the tangents to the untransformed curves at A_0, that is, each transform makes the same angle with the ξ axis as the tangent to the given curve at A_0 makes with the u axis. (The orientation of the ξ and η axes is somewhat unconventional, since one would ordinarily make the ξ axis horizontal.) In the figure, we have taken the positive ξ axis to coincide with the negative w axis, and the positive η axis to coincide with the negative u axis. This has been done for convenience but is not necessary. It is only necessary that the axes of u and η and those of ξ and w be respectively parallel or antiparallel.

Within a narrow region about A_0, the two curves are practically indistinguishable from their respective tangents. Let the point A_1 be chosen on one of the curves, v_1, within this region. Its transform A_1' is chosen so that the projection of A_0A_1 upon the u axis has the same length as the projection of $A_0'A_1'$ upon the ξ axis. Since the transform has the same slope as the tangent to the given curve at A_0, it follows that the projection of A_0A_1 upon the w axis has the same length as the projection of $A_0'A_1'$ upon the η axis.

Draw the straight line A_1B_1 parallel to the w axis. It intersects the other curve v_2 in B_1. Draw the straight line B_1A_2 parallel to the u axis. It intersects v_1 in A_2. Continuing in this manner, we construct the "staircase" $A_1B_1A_2B_2\ldots A_6B_6\ldots$, with the A's on v_1 and the B's on v_2. Similarly, in the trans-

formed figure, we construct the staircase $A_1'B_1'A_2'B_2'\ldots$
$A_6'B_6'\ldots$ with the A''s on the transform of v_1 and the B''s
on the transform of v_2. Now each point denoted by a primed
symbol is the transform of the point denoted by the corresponding unprimed symbol. A_1B_1 and $A_1'B_1'$ intersect at P_1. Like-

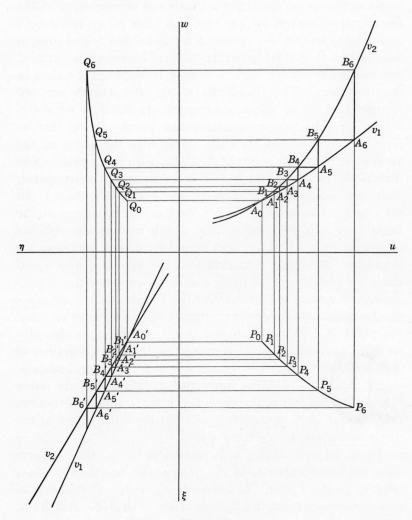

Figure 6.4

wise, A_2B_2 and $A_2'B_2'$ intersect at P_2, and so on. The point P_0 has the same u coordinate as A_0 and the same ξ coordinate as A_0'. A smooth curve $P_0P_1P_2\ldots$ is drawn through the points P_0, P_1, P_2, $\ldots$. This is a plot of ξ against u and should be regarded as a graphical representation of Eq. (6.19). Similarly, we construct the curve $Q_0Q_1Q_2\ldots$, the plot of η against w, which represents Eq. (6.20). Once these two curves have been constructed, the transformation of any curve $v =$ constant does not present any difficulties.

By constructing a second staircase in the given and the transformed figure, we can extend the curve $P_0P_1P_2\ldots$ backwards beyond P_0, and we can extend the curve $Q_0Q_1Q_2\ldots$ backwards beyond Q_0.

Near P_0, the plotted points are sufficiently close together, so that satisfactory graphical interpolation with a French curve is possible. But at a greater distance from P_0, the spacing between successive plotted points may increase to such an extent that graphical interpolation becomes too inaccurate. The same usually applies to the Q's. This can be remedied if an auxiliary staircase is interlaced between the steps of the original staircase. Its starting point is chosen on either curve $v =$ constant in that region where graphical interpolation is sufficiently accurate. The transform of the starting point is determined with the aid of that portion of the P or Q curve which is already known sufficiently accurately. An auxiliary staircase is then also interlaced between the steps of the staircase between the transforms. From the two auxiliary staircases, additional points for the P and Q curves can be obtained as before. If necessary, several such auxiliary staircases may be constructed.

When the curves $v =$ constant show a maximum or minimum of w as a function of u, this method breaks down. In that case, w should first be plotted against v with u as a parameter, so that the roles of u and v are interchanged. The above method may then be applied as before. This device is helpful only if the curves $v =$ constant do not possess an envelope.

6.4. Slope of the Transforms

After Fig. 6.4 has been constructed, the portion below the η and u axes may be stretched in the ξ direction. This does not affect the validity of the construction. Likewise, the portion to the left of the w and ξ axes may be stretched in the η direction; or both such stretches may be performed on the same diagram, even in such a manner that the proportions of the transformed figure in the lower left quadrant remain unchanged. Any of these stretches may be performed when only the figure in the upper right quadrant has been constructed. Thus the proportions of the figures in the other three quadrants may be altered in such a manner that congestion is relieved and graphical work is facilitated. These stretches may affect the slopes of the transforms of the curves $v = v_1$ and $v = v_2$, but they will not affect the ratio of the slopes.

PROBLEM 6.6. As an exercise the reader may derive the rules for determining the length of the line segment $A_0'A_1'$ after such a stretch.

In fact, a change in the length of $A_0'A_1'$ is tantamount to a stretch. However, if staircases are to be constructed on both sides of A_0 and A_0', care must be taken not to subject two portions of the figure in the lower left quadrant to unequal stretches, or the transforms of curves not going through A_0 may have a cusp (kink).

Why did we require that the ratio of the slopes of the curves $v = v_1$ and $v = v_2$ at the point of intersection A_0 must not be altered by the anamorphosis? To answer this question, we shall subject the transform in the $\xi\eta$ plane to a second anamorphosis, again transforming the two curves $v = v_1$ and $v = v_2$ into straight lines, but this time without requiring that the ratio of their slopes must remain unchanged. The result of two anamorphoses of the form described by Eqs. (6.19) and (6.20) could have been obtained by a single anamorphosis of the same form. The use of two successive anamorphoses is merely a device to facilitate an understanding of the effect of slope of the transforms.

Before performing the second anamorphosis, we shall translate the figure so that the point of intersection A_0' of the two straight lines falls at the origin. This does not constitute a loss of generality. In fact, a translation of coordinates is an anamorphosis of the form of Eqs. (6.19) and (6.20). The figure

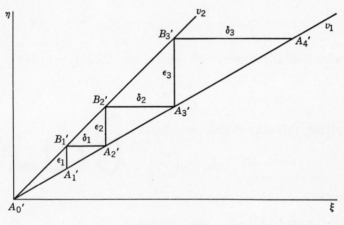

Figure 6.5

may also be stretched as before to bring out detail. The result is shown in Fig. 6.5. Now let the equations of the two lines be

$$\eta = a_1'\xi \qquad (6.22)$$

and

$$\eta = a_2'\xi, \qquad (6.23)$$

so that a_1' and a_2' are the respective slopes of the lines $v = v_1$ and $v = v_2$. Let the coordinates of A_1' be ξ_1, η_1, those of B_1', $\xi_1, \eta_1 + \epsilon_1$, and those of A_2', $\xi_1 + \delta_1, \eta_1 + \epsilon_1$. In general, we shall denote the coordinates of A_n' by ξ_n, η_n. We shall denote the lengths of the line segments $A_n'B_n'$ and $B_n'A_{n+1}'$ by ϵ_n and δ_n respectively. Now, from Eqs. (6.22) and (6.23), we have

$$\epsilon_n = (a_2' - a_1')\xi_n. \qquad (6.24)$$

The angle $A_n'A_{n+1}'B_n'$ is the inclination of the line $v = v_1$, and the tangent of the angle is the slope of this line.   Hence

$$\frac{A_n'B_n'}{B_n'A_{n+1}'} = \frac{\epsilon_n}{\delta_n} = a_1'. \tag{6.25}$$

Similarly, we obtain

$$\frac{A_n'B_n'}{B_{n-1}'A_n'} = \frac{\epsilon_n}{\delta_{n-1}} = a_2'. \tag{6.26}$$

Eliminating ϵ_n between Eqs. (6.25) and (6.26), we obtain

$$\frac{\delta_n}{\delta_{n-1}} = \frac{a_2'}{a_1'}. \tag{6.27}$$

Applying this repeatedly, we obtain

$$\delta_n = \left(\frac{a_2'}{a_1'}\right)^{n-1} \delta_1, \tag{6.28}$$

whence

$$\xi_n = \xi_1 + \delta_1 + \delta_2 + \delta_3 + \ldots\ldots + \delta_{n-1}$$

$$= \xi_1 + \delta_1 \left[1 + \frac{a_2'}{a_1'} + \left(\frac{a_2'}{a_1'}\right)^2 + \ldots\ldots + \left(\frac{a_2'}{a_1'}\right)^{n-2}\right]$$

$$= \xi_1 + \delta_1 \times \frac{\left(\frac{a_2'}{a_1'}\right)^{n-1} - 1}{\frac{a_2'}{a_1'} - 1}. \tag{6.29}$$

Writing $n = 1$ in Eqs. (6.24) and (6.25), eliminating ϵ_1, and solving for δ_1, we obtain in succession:

$$\epsilon_1 = (a_2' - a_1')\xi_1, \tag{6.30}$$

$$\frac{\epsilon_1}{\delta_1} = a_1', \tag{6.31}$$

$$\delta_1 = \xi_1 \left(\frac{a_2'}{a_1'} - 1\right). \tag{6.32}$$

Substituting this into Eq. (6.29), we obtain

$$\xi_n = \xi_1 \left(\frac{a_2'}{a_1'}\right)^{n-1}. \tag{6.33}$$

From Eq. (6.26):

$$\frac{\epsilon_{n+1}}{\delta_n} = a_2'. \tag{6.34}$$

From this and (6.25):

$$\frac{\epsilon_{n+1}}{\epsilon_n} = \frac{a_2'}{a_1'}. \tag{6.35}$$

Hence

$$\epsilon_n = \left(\frac{a_2'}{a_1'}\right)^{n-1} \epsilon_1 \tag{6.36}$$

and

$$\eta_n = \eta_1 + \epsilon_1 + \epsilon_2 + \epsilon_3 + \ldots \ldots + \epsilon_{n-1}$$

$$= \eta_1 + \epsilon_1 \left[1 + \frac{a_2'}{a_1'} + \left(\frac{a_2'}{a_1'}\right)^2 + \ldots \ldots + \left(\frac{a_2'}{a_1'}\right)^{n-2}\right]$$

$$= \eta_1 + \epsilon_1 \frac{\left(\frac{a_2'}{a_1'}\right)^{n-1} - 1}{\frac{a_2'}{a_1'} - 1}. \tag{6.37}$$

From Eq. (6.22):

$$\eta_1 = a_1' \xi_1. \tag{6.38}$$

Eliminating ξ_1 and δ_1 between Eqs. (6.38), (6.32), and (6.31), we obtain

$$\epsilon_1 = \eta_1 \left(\frac{a_2'}{a_1'} - 1\right). \tag{6.39}$$

Substituting this into Eq. (6.37), we obtain

$$\eta_n = \eta_1 \left(\frac{a_2'}{a_1'}\right)^{n-1}. \tag{6.40}$$

Since the staircase construction applies also after the second anamorphosis, the same reasoning and conclusions apply to the transform as well. We shall use double primes to distinguish corresponding quantities after the second anamorphosis. Then in place of Eqs. (6.33) and (6.40), we have

$$\xi_n'' = \xi_1'' \left(\frac{a_2''}{a_1''}\right)^{n-1}, \tag{6.41}$$

$$\eta_n'' = \eta_1'' \left(\frac{a_2''}{a_1''}\right)^{n-1}. \tag{6.42}$$

By the staircase construction, any given value of n identifies corresponding values of ξ_n and ξ_n'', so that ξ_n'' can be expressed as a function of ξ_n. Taking logarithms of Eqs. (6.33) and (6.41), we obtain

$$\log \xi_n = \log \xi_1 + (n-1) \log \frac{a_2'}{a_1'}, \tag{6.43}$$

$$\log \xi_n'' = \log \xi_1'' + (n-1) \log \frac{a_2''}{a_1''}. \tag{6.44}$$

Eliminating n between these two equations, solving for ξ_n'', and taking antilogarithms, we obtain

$$\xi_n'' = \frac{\xi_n{}^k \xi_1''}{\xi_1{}^k}, \tag{6.45}$$

where

$$k = \frac{\log \dfrac{a_2''}{a_1''}}{\log \dfrac{a_2'}{a_1'}}. \tag{6.46}$$

Since we eventually interpolate between the points of the staircase construction, we may omit the subscript n in Eq. (6.45), so that

$$\xi'' = \frac{\xi^k \xi_1''}{\xi_1{}^k}. \tag{6.47}$$

Similarly, starting from Eqs. (6.40) and (6.42), we obtain

$$\eta'' = \frac{\eta^k \eta_1''}{\eta_1{}^k}. \tag{6.48}$$

The transformation represented by Eqs. (6.47) and (6.48) will transform a straight line not passing through the origin into a straight line if and only if $k = 1$, that is

$$\frac{a_2''}{a_1''} = \frac{a_2'}{a_1'}. \tag{6.49}$$

Hence the requirement that the ratio of these two slopes must be invariant.

If $k > 1$, a straight line in the $\xi\eta$ plane not passing through A_0' transforms into a curve in the $\xi''\eta''$ plane of the type sketched in Fig. 6.6, that is, it is tangent to those straight lines which have

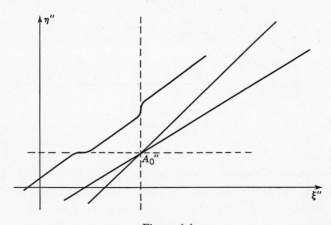

Figure 6.6

the same abscissa or ordinate as the point of intersection A_0'' (shown dotted in the figure).   If $k < 1$, the transform will be of the type sketched in Fig. 6.7, that is, it intersects the dotted lines at right angles.   If the original figure in the uv system of Fig. 6.4 was plotted from empirical data, the ratio of the slopes a_2'/a_1' must be determined graphically.   Any inaccuracy in this graphical determination will then be betrayed by deformations of the curves in the transform as shown in Figs. 6.6 or 6.7; and by identifying one or the other type of deformation, the nomographer can determine whether a_2'/a_1' was taken too large or too small. Only if all curves $v = $ constant are concurrent, or if all their points of intersection lie outside the region of interest, is the value of a_2'/a_1' not critical.

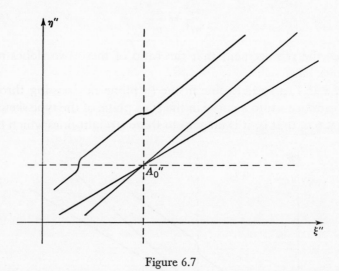

Figure 6.7

The dotted lines in Figs. 6.6 and 6.7 are not necessarily the coordinate axes, since a translation of coordinates does not invalidate the staircase construction. In this section, we have taken these dotted lines as the coordinate axes only to simplify the algebra.

CHAPTER VII

Kellogg's Method

7.1. Wronskians

In the present chapter, we shall have so much occasion to deal with partial derivatives that it will be desirable to introduce a shorthand notation. We shall accordingly use the symbol denoting an independent variable as a subscript to indicate partial differentiation with respect to that variable. For instance, we shall write f_x in place of $\partial f/\partial x$, or f_{xx} in place of $\partial^2 f/\partial x^2$, or f_{xy} in place of $\partial^2 f/\partial x \partial y$. We shall assume throughout that we are dealing with "well-behaved" functions, which possess all the required derivatives and for which the order of differentiation is immaterial, so that $f_{xy} = f_{yx}$, and so on. This notation is at variance with that used in Eqs. (2.7) and (2.8) and in Chapter IV. Numbers will be used as subscripts as before to distinguish between different quantities.

We shall say that four functions $f_1(x)$, $f_2(x)$, $f_3(x)$, $f_4(x)$ are linearly related if there exist four nonzero quantities c_1, c_2, c_3, c_4 independent of x such that

$$c_1 f_1 + c_2 f_2 + c_3 f_3 + c_4 f_4 = 0. \tag{7.1}$$

A corresponding defining equation involving n terms holds when n functions are linearly related. Although the reasoning which follows is generally applicable to n linearly related functions, we shall continue to use the case of four functions as an illustrative example in order to avoid the ambiguous use of n as a subscript.

In order to determine whether the four functions are linearly related, we differentiate Eq. (7.1) three times:

$$c_1 f_1 + c_2 f_2 + c_3 f_3 + c_4 f_4 = 0 \tag{7.1}$$

$$c_1 f_{1x} + c_2 f_{2x} + c_3 f_{3x} + c_4 f_{4x} = 0 \tag{7.2}$$

$$c_1 f_{1xx} + c_2 f_{2xx} + c_3 f_{3xx} + c_4 f_{4xx} = 0 \tag{7.3}$$

$$c_1 f_{1xxx} + c_2 f_{2xxx} + c_3 f_{3xxx} + c_4 f_{4xxx} = 0. \tag{7.4}$$

By Theorem 1.8 there exist four such nonzero quantities c_1, c_2, c_3, c_4 if and only if

$$\begin{vmatrix} f_1 & f_2 & f_3 & f_4 \\ f_{1x} & f_{2x} & f_{3x} & f_{4x} \\ f_{1xx} & f_{2xx} & f_{3xx} & f_{4xx} \\ f_{1xxx} & f_{2xxx} & f_{3xxx} & f_{4xxx} \end{vmatrix} = 0. \tag{7.5}$$

The determinant in Eq. (7.5) is called the wronskian of the four functions. We therefore have:

THEOREM 7.1. A set of functions of a single variable are linearly related if and only if their wronskian vanishes.

Of course, we could have obtained a condition involving derivatives of order higher than the third by continuing to differentiate Eq. (7.4); but since Eq. (7.5) is a sufficient condition for a linear relationship between the four functions, further differentiation would not teach us anything new. By Theorem 1.4, we may interchange the roles of rows and columns in the wronskian without changing its value.

Consider now a set of functions of two variables v and w. If there are more than two functions in the set, the vanishing of the two wronskians (those involving partial derivatives with respect to v or w respectively) is a necessary but not sufficient condition for the existence of a linear relationship; for the vanishing of the one wronskian tells us only that the coefficients c in Eq. (7.1) cannot be functions of v, and the vanishing of the other tells us that the c's cannot be functions of w. However, it does not follow that a single set of constant coefficients can be found which satisfy Eq. (7.1).   Instead, there may be two sets, one consisting of functions of w, the other, of functions of v.

The case of just two functions is the lone exception.   For if

$$\begin{vmatrix} f_1 & f_{1v} \\ f_2 & f_{2v} \end{vmatrix} = 0, \qquad (7.6)$$

then

$$\frac{f_1}{f_2} = \frac{c_2}{c_1} = c \qquad (7.7)$$

cannot depend on v.   Likewise, if

$$\begin{vmatrix} f_1 & f_{1w} \\ f_2 & f_{2w} \end{vmatrix} = 0, \qquad (7.8)$$

then c in Eq. (7.7) cannot depend on w.   Hence, if both Eqs. (7.6) and (7.8) are satisfied, c in Eq. (7.7) must be a constant. It may then be proved as in the derivation of Eq. (7.5) that, in addition,

$$\begin{vmatrix} f_{1v} & f_{1w} \\ f_{2v} & f_{2w} \end{vmatrix} = 0. \qquad (7.9)$$

It follows that Eqs. (7.6), (7.8), and (7.9) together form a necessary and sufficient condition for a linear relationship between the functions $f_1(v, w)$ and $f_2(v, w)$; but Eqs. (7.6) and (7.8) without (7.9) would also have been necessary and sufficient.

From any matrix, we may form a variety of square matrices by deleting rows and/or columns, and each of these square matrices has a determinant associated with it.   We define the rank of a (not necessarily square) matrix to be the order of the highest-order determinant contained in it which does not vanish identically.   We may now combine the conditions (7.6), (7.8), and (7.9) into one.

THEOREM 7.2. If $f_1(v, w)$ and $f_2(v, w)$ are to be linearly related, it is necessary and sufficient that the rank of the matrix

$$[M_2] = \begin{bmatrix} f_1 & f_{1v} & f_{1w} \\ f_2 & f_{2v} & f_{2w} \end{bmatrix} \tag{7.10}$$

be less than 2. Passing now to the case of three functions, we have the proposition:

THEOREM 7.3. Three functions f_1, f_2, and f_3 depending on only two variables v and w are linearly related if and only if the rank of the matrix

$$[M_3] = \begin{bmatrix} f_1 & f_{1v} & f_{1w} & f_{1vv} & f_{1vw} & f_{1ww} \\ f_2 & f_{2v} & f_{2w} & f_{2vv} & f_{2vw} & f_{2ww} \\ f_3 & f_{3v} & f_{3w} & f_{3vv} & f_{3vw} & f_{3ww} \end{bmatrix} \tag{7.11}$$

is less than three.

PROBLEM 7.1. The proof of necessity of this condition is similar to the proof of Theorem 7.1 and is left as an exercise for the reader.

The proof of sufficiency is carried out by induction. In all discussions of linearly related functions, we shall rule out the degenerate case where any of the functions vanish identically, although we do not rule out the case of a function some or all of whose derivatives vanish identically.

To prove sufficiency of the condition in Theorem 7.3, we consider first the case where no two of the three functions by themselves are linearly related. Then at least one of the second-order determinants contained in the matrix $[M_2]$ does not vanish. Let us now select from $[M_3]$ two columns whose first two rows form such a nonvanishing determinant. By deleting the first, second, and third rows from these two columns, we obtain three determinants which we shall denote respectively by A, $-B$, and C. We know, then, that C does not vanish. By combining these two columns with each of the columns of $[M_3]$ in turn, we obtain a set of third-order determinants, every one of which must vanish, by hypothesis. Let each of these determinants be expanded in terms of the cofactors A, B, C. Then we have:

$$f_1 A + f_2 B + f_3 C = 0 \tag{7.12}$$

$$f_{1v} A + f_{2v} B + f_{3v} C = 0 \tag{7.13}$$

$$f_{1w}A + f_{2w}B + f_{3w}C = 0 \tag{7.14}$$

$$f_{1vv}A + f_{2vv}B + f_{3vv}C = 0 \tag{7.15}$$

$$f_{1vw}A + f_{2vw}B + f_{3vw}C = 0 \tag{7.16}$$

$$f_{1ww}A + f_{2ww}B + f_{3ww}C = 0. \tag{7.17}$$

Two of these equations hold by virtue of Theorem 1.3, the others by hypothesis.

Let Eqs. (7.12) through (7.14) be differentiated with respect to v. We obtain:

$$f_{1v}A + f_{2v}B + f_{3v}C + f_1 A_v + f_2 B_v + f_3 C_v = 0 \tag{7.18}$$

$$f_{1vv}A + f_{2vv}B + f_{3vv}C + f_{1v}A_v + f_{2v}B_v + f_{3v}C_v = 0 \tag{7.19}$$

$$f_{1vw}A + f_{2vw}B + f_{3vw}C + f_{1w}A_v + f_{2w}B_v + f_{3w}C_v = 0. \tag{7.20}$$

Eliminating A, B, and C (but not their derivatives) from these equations with the aid of Eqs. (7.13), (7.15), and (7.16), we obtain

$$f_1 A_v + f_2 B_v + f_3 C_v = 0 \tag{7.21}$$

$$f_{1v}A_v + f_{2v}B_v + f_{3v}C_v = 0 \tag{7.22}$$

$$f_{1w}A_v + f_{2w}B_v + f_{3w}C_v = 0. \tag{7.23}$$

It will be seen that these equations are of the same form as Eqs. (7.12), (7.13), and (7.14), but A, B, and C have been replaced with their partial derivatives with respect to v.

Let Eqs. (7.12), (7.13), and (7.14) be regarded as homogeneous equations for determination of the unknowns A, B, C. Since the determinant of their coefficients vanishes, the equations are compatible and nonzero solutions are possible. We know already that C does not vanish identically. Suppose now that A and B are also nonzero. Having obtained any solution A, B, C, we can obtain any other by multiplying A, B, and C by a common factor. Since A_v, B_v, and C_v satisfy the same equations as A, B, and C, we must have

$$\frac{A_v}{A} = \frac{B_v}{B} = \frac{C_v}{C}. \tag{7.24}$$

Integrating these with respect to v, we obtain

$$\ln A - \ln k_1 = \ln B - \ln k_2 = \ln C - \ln k_3, \qquad (7.25)$$

where the k's are constants of integration independent of v. Hence the ratios A/C and B/C are independent of v, and a similar argument shows that they are independent of w. Dividing Eq. (7.12) through by C, we obtain a linear relationship between f_1, f_2, f_3 with constant coefficients, and the proposition is proved.

If A vanishes identically, the same reasoning will prove a linear relationship between f_2 and f_3 contrary to hypothesis. Similarly, if $B = 0$, then f_1 and f_3 must be linearly related. If A and B both vanish identically, it follows that f_3 vanishes identically, contrary to hypothesis. These cases may therefore be ruled out.

If f_1 and f_2 are linearly related, any second-order determinant contained in the first two rows of $[M_3]$ equals zero. Then any third-order determinant contained in $[M_3]$ will have all co-factors of elements in the third row equal to zero, so that the determinant itself must vanish. Thus, we have exhausted all possibilities.

If there exist two linear relationships between three functions, each of the three can be eliminated in turn, so that any two of the three functions will also be linearly related. In this case, the matrix $[M_3]$ will be of rank one.

Similar theorems can be proved for a linear relationship between more than three functions. We shall be concerned only with the case of four functions, and we have:

THEOREM 7.4. Four functions f_1, f_2, f_3, f_4 depending on only two variables v and w are linearly related if and only if the matrix

$$[M_4] = \begin{bmatrix} f_1 & f_{1v} & f_{1w} & f_{1vv} & f_{1vw} & f_{1ww} & f_{1vvv} & f_{1vvw} & f_{1vww} & f_{1www} \\ f_2 & f_{2v} & f_{2w} & f_{2vv} & f_{2vw} & f_{2ww} & f_{2vvv} & f_{2vvw} & f_{2vww} & f_{2www} \\ f_3 & f_{3v} & f_{3w} & f_{3vv} & f_{3vw} & f_{3ww} & f_{3vvv} & f_{3vvw} & f_{3vww} & f_{3www} \\ f_4 & f_{4v} & f_{4w} & f_{4vv} & f_{4vw} & f_{4ww} & f_{4vvv} & f_{4vvw} & f_{4vww} & f_{4www} \end{bmatrix}$$

$$(7.26)$$

is of rank lower than four.   In particular, if there exist two linear relationships between the four functions, the matrix $[M_4]$ is of rank two, and if there exist three linear relationships, $[M_4]$ is of rank one.

PROBLEM 7.2. The proof is again carried out by induction, starting from Theorem 7.3, and is left as an exercise.

7.2. *Differential Equations*

A thorough treatment of differential equations is beyond the scope of this book but will be found in specialized textbooks. The treatment given here is of necessity somewhat simplified by omission.

We shall be concerned only with the homogeneous linear differential equation of the third order

$$g_{uuu}Q_3 + g_{uu}Q_2 + g_u Q_1 + g Q_0 = 0, \qquad (7.27)$$

where $g(u)$ is a function to be determined, and the Q's are given functions of u.   A function $g(u)$ which satisfies Eq. (7.27) is called a solution of the differential equation.   In general, a variety of solutions are possible.

PROBLEM 7.3. By substituting a linear combination of several functions in place of g in Eq. (7.27), the reader may prove as an exercise that any linear combination of solutions is itself a solution of Eq. (7.27).

Under fairly general conditions, the following theorem can be proved.

THEOREM 7.5. If g, g_u, and g_{uu} are arbitrarily prescribed for any one value of u, the solution $g(u)$ is uniquely determined.   ,

A determination of the required solution by analytical methods is frequently difficult, if it is possible at all.   Indeed, many differential equations cannot be solved in terms of elementary functions.   We shall give a numerical process whereby a solution satisfying the given initial conditions can be obtained approximately in tabular form.

Knowing the values of g, g_u, and g_{uu} at a given value of u, we can solve Eq. (7.27) for g_{uuu}.   Assuming that g_{uuu} is approximately constant over a narrow range Δu of values of the independent variable, we have

$$g_{uu}(u + \Delta u) = g_{uu}(u) + g_{uuu}(u)\Delta u. \qquad (7.28)$$

Similarly

$$g_u(u + \Delta u) = g_u(u) + g_{uu}(u)\Delta u \qquad (7.29)$$

and

$$g(u + \Delta u) = g(u) + g_u(u)\Delta u. \qquad (7.30)$$

Using the values of g, g_u, and g_{uu} at $u + \Delta u$ as initial values, we repeat the process to obtain their values at $u + 2\Delta u$, and so on. The smaller the increment Δu, the greater the accuracy of the process. As Δu tends to zero, the approximate solution approaches the true solution. By a refinement of this line of reasoning, Theorem 7.5 could be demonstrated rigorously.

THEOREM 7.6. In particular, it will be found by direct substitution in Eq. (7.27) that $g \equiv 0$ is a solution of this equation. It has the property of vanishing, together with all its derivatives, at any value of u. Now Theorem 7.5 tells us that there exists one and only one solution which vanishes together with its first and second derivatives at any given value of u. This solution must therefore vanish identically. This proposition will be referred to as Theorem 7.6.

Next, we prove:

THEOREM 7.7. If the wronskian of three solutions of Eq. (7.27) vanishes for any value of u, it must vanish identically.

Proof: Consider a function $f(u)$, a linear combination of three solutions U_1, U_2, U_3 of Eq. (7.27), and its first and second derivatives:

$$f = c_1 U_1 + c_2 U_2 + c_3 U_3 \qquad (7.31)$$

$$f_u = c_1 U_{1u} + c_2 U_{2u} + c_3 U_{3u} \qquad (7.32)$$

$$f_{uu} = c_1 U_{1uu} + c_2 U_{2uu} + c_3 U_{3uu}. \qquad (7.33)$$

We showed in Problem 7.3 that f must be a solution of Eq. (7.27). If, at some particular value of u, the wronskian of the three U's vanishes, then, by Theorem 1.8, nonzero values for c_1, c_2, and c_3 can be chosen so that f, f_u, and f_{uu} vanish at this value of u. But, by Theorem 7.6, f must then vanish identically. Therefore, by Theorem 7.1, the wronskian of U_1, U_2, and U_3 must vanish identically.

To conclude this section, we demonstrate:

THEOREM 7.8. Any solution $g = f(u)$ of Eq. (7.27) which is prescribed together with its first two derivatives at a given value of u can be expressed as a linear combination of three linearly independent solutions U_1, U_2, U_3.

Proof: Substituting the prescribed initial values of f, f_u, and f_{uu} into Eqs. (7.31), (7.32), and (7.33), we may solve for c_1, c_2, c_3 (by Eq. (1.11)). Hence f is determined in terms of the U's for all values of u.

7.3. First Necessary Condition for a Nomogram

We now come to the problem of ascertaining whether a given equation

$$g\ (u, v, w) = 0 \tag{7.34}$$

can be nomographed, and if so, to construct the nomogram. Two methods for accomplishing this have been described, one due to T. H. Gronwall, the other, to O. D. Kellogg. (See bibliography at the end of this book.) Gronwall's method is by far the more difficult and advanced and is therefore unsuitable for inclusion in this book. For the construction of a nomogram, it requires the solving of two simultaneous nonlinear partial differential equations, which frequently cannot be done in terms of classical functions. Nonetheless, Gronwall's method is not entirely useless. Kellogg's method, which shall concern us during the balance of this chapter, can only ascertain whether a given equation of the form (7.34) can be nomographed *as it stands*. For instance, the equation in Problem 2.11 cannot be nomographed as it stands; but if we take logarithms of both sides of the equation, it will thereby be brought into a form which can be represented by a nomogram. Only previous knowledge or a hunch, but not Kellogg's method, would have indicated that the device of taking the logarithm would lead to success. When Gronwall's method is used, no previous knowledge or hunches are necessary; but, as we have already pointed out, greater difficulties arise elsewhere instead. Some of Gronwall's results will be given in Chapter VIII.

The immediate problem of the nomographer is to rewrite Eq. (7.34) in the form of Eq. (2.8). In order not to give the impression that the subscripts indicate partial differentiation, we shall rewrite Eqs. (7.34) and (2.8) in the notation

$$g(u, v, w) = \begin{vmatrix} \rho_1 & \rho_2 & \rho_3 \\ \sigma_1 & \sigma_2 & \sigma_3 \\ \tau_1 & \tau_2 & \tau_3 \end{vmatrix} = 0, \tag{7.35}$$

where the ρ's depend on u only, the σ's on v only, and the τ's on w only. The expansion of this determinant is a linear combination of the ρ's, or of the σ's, or of the τ's. In other words, the functions g, ρ_1, ρ_2, and ρ_3 are linearly related with coefficients independent of u but depending on v and w. If ρ_1, ρ_2, and ρ_3 are not linearly related, then g must be the solution of a homogeneous linear third-order differential equation in u, that is an equation of the same form as Eq. (7.27), where the Q's depend on u only. This follows from Theorem 7.8. The ρ's will be three different linear combinations of the U's with coefficients independent of u, v, and w. If, for the moment, we regard only v and w as variables, we can say that g, g_u, g_{uu}, and g_{uuu} are linearly related by Eq. (7.27). By Theorem 7.4, we know that this will happen if and only if the matrix

$$[M_5] = \begin{bmatrix} g & g_v & g_w & g_{vv} \cdots\cdots g_{www} \\ g_u & g_{uv} & g_{uw} & g_{uvv} \cdots\cdots g_{uwww} \\ g_{uu} & g_{uuv} & g_{uuw} & g_{uuvv} \cdots\cdots g_{uuwww} \\ g_{uuu} & g_{uuuv} & g_{uuuw} & g_{uuuvv} \cdots\cdots g_{uuuwww} \end{bmatrix} \tag{7.36}$$

is of rank lower than four. If there exist two linear relations between g, g_u, g_{uu}, and g_{uuu} with coefficients depending on u only, we may eliminate g_{uuu} between them and obtain a homogeneous second-order linear differential equation. This has only two linearly independent solutions, so that ρ_1, ρ_2, and ρ_3 must be linearly related. In this case, the matrix $[M_5]$ must be of rank 2. There exists even the possibility that two linear relationships exist between ρ_1, ρ_2, and ρ_3; however, this is of no interest to nomography, as we shall see. Given the function g, we can always construct the matrix $[M_5]$ and determine its rank. If this is less than four, a linear relation exists between g, g_u, g_{uu}, and g_{uuu}, and its coefficients (the Q's of Eq. (7.27)) may be determined as described in Section 7.1. Three suitable linearly independent functions of u which are solutions of Eq. (7.27) may then be determined by any means whatever. Usually, this can be done by inspection of Eq. (7.34). In fact, it is not necessary to construct the matrix $[M_5]$ and to determine its rank, unless there is doubt as to whether Eq. (7.34) can be nomographed at all. Let the three linearly independent solutions of Eq. (7.27) be denoted by U_1, U_2, and U_3. The desired functions ρ_1, ρ_2, and ρ_3 must be linear combinations of these. We shall postpone for the moment the question whether it is possible to have $\rho_1 = U_1$, $\rho_2 = U_2$, and $\rho_3 = U_3$.

Our reasoning concerning the dependence of g on u is equally applicable to the dependence of g on v or on w. We shall define a matrix $[M_6]$ obtained from $[M_5]$ by interchanging the roles of u and v, and a matrix $[M_7]$ obtained from $[M_5]$ by interchanging the roles of u and w. By the same reasoning as above, $[M_6]$ and $[M_7]$ must be of rank lower than four. The three conditions concerning the ranks of the matrices $[M_5]$, $[M_6]$, and $[M_7]$ are then necessary but not sufficient for a nomographic representation of Eq. (7.34). For instance, the equation

$$u^2v^2 + v^3w^2 + wu^2 - wv^2 - v^3u - u^2w^2 = 0 \qquad (7.37)$$

satisfies these three conditions, but it cannot be nomographed, as we shall see in the next section.

Just as we represented g as a linear combination of three functions U_1, U_2, and U_3 which depend only on u, so we must represent it as a linear combination of three functions V_1, V_2, and V_3 which depend only on v, or of three functions W_1, W_2, and W_3 which depend only on w. Then the σ's in Eq. (7.35) are linear combinations of the V's, and the τ's are linear combinations of the W's. However, it does not follow that

$$g = \begin{vmatrix} U_1 & U_2 & U_3 \\ V_1 & V_2 & V_3 \\ W_1 & W_2 & W_3 \end{vmatrix}. \tag{7.38}$$

In fact, in general, this is untrue. At best, we could subject Eq. (7.35) to the transformation of Section 4.3, choosing the k's so that the first row of the determinant becomes U_1, U_2, U_3. The assumption that $\rho_1 = U_1$, $\rho_2 = U_2$, and $\rho_3 = U_3$ is therefore justified; but it is not true in general that $\sigma_1 = V_1$, $\sigma_2 = V_2$, ..., $\tau_3 = W_3$. It may happen that one of the U's, V's, and/or W's is a constant. This does not constitute a loss of generality.

The case where a linear relation exists between the U's, between the V's, and/or between the W's will be postponed until Section 7.5.

7.4. Second Condition for a Nomogram

When we have determined the ρ's, we may write g in the form

$$g = \rho_1 J_1 + \rho_2 J_2 + \rho_3 J_3, \tag{7.39}$$

where the J's are functions of v and w only. Expanding the determinant in Eq. (7.35) in terms of cofactors of the ρ's, we see that the J's are these cofactors.

PROBLEM 7.4. The reader may prove as an exercise that

$$\sigma_1 J_1 + \sigma_2 J_2 + \sigma_3 J_3 = 0 \tag{7.40}$$

and

$$\tau_1 J_1 + \tau_2 J_2 + \tau_3 J_3 = 0. \tag{7.41}$$

Equation (7.40) states that the J's are linearly related with coefficients independent of w, and (7.41) states that the J's are linearly related with coefficients independent of v. Hence, by Theorem 7.1, we have:

$$\begin{vmatrix} J_1 & J_2 & J_3 \\ J_{1w} & J_{2w} & J_{3w} \\ J_{1ww} & J_{2ww} & J_{3ww} \end{vmatrix} = 0 \qquad (7.42)$$

and

$$\begin{vmatrix} J_1 & J_2 & J_3 \\ J_{1v} & J_{2v} & J_{3v} \\ J_{1vv} & J_{2vv} & J_{3vv} \end{vmatrix} = 0. \qquad (7.43)$$

These are also necessary conditions for the existence of a nomogram.

PROBLEM 7.5. Prove that Eq. (7.37) cannot be nomographed.

Assuming as before that the U's, V's, and W's each form a linearly independent set, we must determine the ρ's, σ's, and τ's. We showed already that we may identify the ρ's with the respective U's. Knowing the expressions for g and the ρ's, we obtain the expressions for the J's by inspection from Eq. (7.39). When the expressions for the J's are substituted into Eq. (7.40), this equation will be linear in the three W's. Since the W's are linearly independent, Eq. (7.40) can hold for all values of w only if the coefficients of the W's vanish individually. Equating these three coefficients individually to zero, we obtain three homogeneous equations for the determination of the three unknowns σ_1, σ_2, σ_3. These equations will have nonzero solutions if Eq. (7.42) is satisfied.

Since the equations are homogeneous in the σ's, one of the σ's may be chosen arbitrarily, for instance $\sigma_3 = 1$. The equations may then be solved* for σ_1 and σ_2. Similarly, we determine the τ's. In this manner, the nomogram can be obtained.

PROBLEM 7.6. Nomograph the equation

---

* Kellogg's statement that the σ's are the cofactors of the J's in the determinant of Eq. (7.42) except for a common multiplicative factor is incorrect except in special cases.

$u^2(e^v + w \cos v + \ln w \cos v + \cos v - w - \ln w) + \sin u$

$(we^v + e^v - 1 - 2 \ln w - w - \cos v - \ln w \cos v - w \cos v)$

$+ \ln w \cos v + 2w + 2 \ln w - we^v - e^v - \cos v = 0.$

Could this be solved by the method of Section 2.5? Why?

7.5. Degenerate Cases

So far, we have only considered the case where ρ_1, ρ_2, ρ_3 in Eq. (7.35) are linearly independent, and similarly for the σ's and the τ's. We now come to the degenerate cases where not all these conditions are satisfied. Taking the ρ's as an example, there may exist one or two linear relationships between them. We shall first dispose of the latter case. In that case, we can find a transformation of the type discussed in Section 4.3 which will reduce ρ_1 and ρ_2 to zero. By this transformation, Eq. (7.35) is reduced to the form:

$$\begin{vmatrix} 0 & 0 & \rho_3 \\ \sigma_1 & \sigma_2 & \sigma_3 \\ \tau_1 & \tau_2 & \tau_3 \end{vmatrix} = 0. \tag{7.44}$$

Expanding the determinant in terms of cofactors of the first row, we obtain

$$\rho_3 \begin{vmatrix} \sigma_1 & \sigma_2 \\ \tau_1 & \tau_2 \end{vmatrix} = 0. \tag{7.45}$$

Now, a product can vanish only if one of its factors vanishes; that is, we have either

$$\rho_3 = 0 \tag{7.46}$$

or

$$\begin{vmatrix} \sigma_1 & \sigma_2 \\ \tau_1 & \tau_2 \end{vmatrix} = 0. \tag{7.47}$$

In either case, u is not a function of v and w, so that no nomogram is possible. By the same argument, we dispose of the possibility that there may exist two linear relationships between the σ's or between the τ's.

If the elements in one row of the determinant in Eq. (7.35) are linearly independent, we may denote the independent variable on which this row depends by u. This means only a change of notation at most. Now, if the elements in either or both of the other rows are not linearly independent, the method of the preceding section remains valid with only minor changes. Suppose for example that the τ's are linearly related. In that case, they must be linear combinations of two functions W_1 and W_2 of w, and we must have $W_3 = 0$. Using the same reasoning as in the preceding section, we obtain only two equations homogeneous in the σ's, which are just as useful as the three compatible equations obtained previously. Again, we may arbitrarily set one of the three σ's equal to unity. However, if the σ's are linearly related, it may happen that one of them vanishes identically, and care must be taken not to set this one equal to unity. If the three σ's are linearly related, the determination of the τ's proceeds similarly.

PROBLEM 7.7. Nomograph the equation

$$\sin(u - v)\sin(u + v + w) = 0.$$

Hint: If we take $V_1 = \sin^2 v$, $V_2 = \sin v \cos v$, and $V_3 = \cos^2 v$, then any terms independent of v must be expanded in terms of v with the aid of the identity $1 = \sin^2 v + \cos^2 v$.

PROBLEM 7.8. Solve Problem 2.19 by the present method.

There remains the case where the three elements in each row of the determinant are linearly related. In this case we can always choose U_1, U_2, V_1, V_2, W_1, and W_2 so that $U_3 = V_3 = W_3 = 0$. As before, we shall take $\rho_1 = U_1$, $\rho_2 = U_2$, $\rho_3 = U_3 = 0$. Now let

$$\left. \begin{array}{lll} \sigma_1 = a_1V_1 + a_2V_2, & \sigma_2 = b_1V_1 + b_2V_2, & \sigma_3 = c_1V_1 + c_2V_2, \\ \tau_1 = \alpha_1W_1 + \alpha_2W_2, & \tau_2 = \beta_1W_1 + \beta_2W_2, & \tau_3 = \gamma_1W_1 + \gamma_2W_2, \end{array} \right\} \tag{7.48}$$

where a_1, a_2, b_1, b_2, c_1, c_2, α_1, α_2, β_1, β_2, γ_1, γ_2 are constants to be determined. Substituting the ρ's, σ's, and τ's into Eq. (7.35) and expanding in terms of cofactors of the first row, we obtain

$$U_1[(b_1\gamma_1 - c_1\beta_1)V_1W_1 + (b_1\gamma_2 - c_1\beta_2)V_1W_2 + (b_2\gamma_1 - c_2\beta_1)V_2W_1$$
$$+ (b_2\gamma_2 - c_2\beta_2)V_2W_2] + U_2[(c_1\alpha_1 - a_1\gamma_1)V_1W_1 + (c_1\alpha_2 - a_1\gamma_2)V_1W_2$$
$$+ (c_2\alpha_1 - a_2\gamma_1)V_2W_1 + (c_2\alpha_2 - a_2\gamma_2)V_2W_2] = 0. \quad (7.49)$$

The equation to be nomographed will be given in the form

$$U_1[R_1V_1W_1 + R_2V_1W_2 + R_3V_2W_1 + R_4V_2W_2] + U_2[S_1V_1W_1$$
$$+ S_2V_1W_2 + S_3V_2W_1 + S_4V_2W_2] = 0, \quad (7.50)$$

where the R's and S's are given constants. Equating corresponding coefficients in Eqs. (7.49) and (7.50), we obtain

$$b_1\gamma_1 - c_1\beta_1 = R_1, \quad (7.51)$$

$$b_1\gamma_2 - c_1\beta_2 = R_2, \quad (7.52)$$

$$b_2\gamma_1 - c_2\beta_1 = R_3, \quad (7.53)$$

$$b_2\gamma_2 - c_2\beta_2 = R_4, \quad (7.54)$$

$$c_1\alpha_1 - a_1\gamma_1 = S_1, \quad (7.55)$$

$$c_1\alpha_2 - a_1\gamma_2 = S_2, \quad (7.56)$$

$$c_2\alpha_1 - a_2\gamma_1 = S_3, \quad (7.57)$$

$$c_2\alpha_2 - a_2\gamma_2 = S_4. \quad (7.58)$$

These eight equations are too few to determine uniquely the twelve unknowns. We shall therefore express eight of them in terms of the other four, leaving aside for the moment the choice of values for the latter. We shall accordingly regard α_1, β_1, γ_1, and c_1 as known.

Multiplying Eq. (7.51) by γ_2 and (7.52) by γ_1 and subtracting, we obtain

$$c_1(\gamma_1\beta_2 - \gamma_2\beta_1) = R_1\gamma_2 - R_2\gamma_1. \quad (7.59)$$

Similarly, from (7.53) and (7.54):

$$c_2(\gamma_1\beta_2 - \gamma_2\beta_1) = R_3\gamma_2 - R_4\gamma_1. \quad (7.60)$$

Multiplying Eq. (7.59) by c_2 and (7.60) by c_1 and subtracting, we obtain

$$\gamma_2(c_2R_1 - c_1R_3) - \gamma_1(c_2R_2 - c_1R_4) = 0. \quad (7.61)$$

Similarly, from Eqs. (7.55) through (7.58), we obtain in succession:

$$c_1(\alpha_1\gamma_2 - \alpha_2\gamma_1) = S_1\gamma_2 - S_2\gamma_1, \qquad (7.62)$$

$$c_2(\alpha_1\gamma_2 - \alpha_2\gamma_1) = S_3\gamma_2 - S_4\gamma_1, \qquad (7.63)$$

$$\gamma_2(c_2 S_1 - c_1 S_3) - \gamma_1(c_2 S_2 - c_1 S_4) = 0. \qquad (7.64)$$

Eliminating γ_2 (and thereby γ_1) between Eqs. (7.61) and (7.64), we obtain a quadratic in c_2. Let

$$c_2 = P_1 c_1 \qquad (7.65)$$

be one of the solutions of this quadratic, where P_1 is a function of the R's and S's. Similarly, we obtain a relation of the form

$$\gamma_2 = P_2\gamma_1, \qquad (7.66)$$

where P_2 is a function of the R's and S's. Solving Eq. (7.61) for γ_2 and then substituting for c_2 and γ_2 from Eqs. (7.65) and (7.66), we obtain

$$P_2 = \frac{P_1 R_2 - R_4}{P_1 R_1 - R_3}. \qquad (7.67)$$

Similarly, from Eq. (7.64), we obtain

$$P_2 = \frac{P_1 S_2 - S_4}{P_1 S_1 - S_3}. \qquad (7.68)$$

Since P_1 can have either of two possible values, so can P_2; but P_2 is a single-valued function of P_1.

Solving Eq. (7.51) for b_1, we obtain:

$$b_1 = \frac{R_1 + c_1\beta_1}{\gamma_1}. \qquad (7.69)$$

From Eqs. (7.52), (7.69), and (7.66), we obtain

$$\beta_2 = \frac{R_1 P_2 + c_1\beta_1 P_2 - R_2}{c_1}. \qquad (7.70)$$

From (7.53) and (7.65):

$$b_2 = \frac{R_3 + c_1\beta_1 P_1}{\gamma_1}. \tag{7.71}$$

Substituting from Eqs. (7.71), (7.70), (7.65), and (7.66) into Eq. (7.54) and solving for P_2, we obtain Eq. (7.67). The solution is therefore self-consistent.

Solving (7.55), we obtain

$$a_1 = \frac{c_1\alpha_1 - S_1}{\gamma_1}. \tag{7.72}$$

From (7.56), (7.72), and (7.66):

$$\alpha_2 = \frac{S_2 + c_1\alpha_1 P_2 - S_1 P_2}{c_1}. \tag{7.73}$$

From (7.57) and (7.65):

$$a_2 = \frac{c_1\alpha_1 P_1 - S_3}{\gamma_1}. \tag{7.74}$$

Finally, from Eqs. (7.58), (7.73), (7.74), (7.65), and (7.66), we obtain Eq. (7.68), showing again that the solution is self-consistent.

Now that the constants have been obtained, we substitute them into Eqs. (7.48), so that Eq. (7.35) takes the form

$$\begin{vmatrix} U_1 & U_2 & 0 \\ \dfrac{c_1\alpha_1 - S_1}{\gamma_1} V_1 & \dfrac{R_1 + c_1\beta_1}{\gamma_1} V_1 & c_1 V_1 \\ + \dfrac{c_1\alpha_1 P_1 - S_3}{\gamma_1} V_2 & + \dfrac{R_3 + c_1\beta_1 P_1}{\gamma_1} V_2 & + c_1 P_1 V_2 \\ \alpha_1 W_1 & \beta_1 W_1 & \gamma_1 W_1 \\ + \dfrac{S_2 + c_1\alpha_1 P_2 - S_1 P_2}{c_1} W_2 & + \dfrac{R_1 P_2 + c_1\beta_1 P_2 - R_2}{c_1} W_2 & + \gamma_1 P_2 W_2 \end{vmatrix}$$
$$= 0. \tag{7.75}$$

On this determinant we perform the following operations in the order listed. Multiply the second row by γ_1. Multiply the third row by c_1. Divide the third column by $c_1\gamma_1$. Subtract from the first column the third column multiplied by $c_1\alpha_1$; that is

$$\sigma_1' = \sigma_1 - c_1\alpha_1\sigma_3, \tag{7.76}$$

$$\tau_1' = \tau_1 - c_1\alpha_1\tau_3. \tag{7.77}$$

Subtract from the second column the third column multiplied by $c_1\beta_1$; that is

$$\sigma_2' = \sigma_2 - c_1\beta_1\sigma_3, \tag{7.78}$$

$$\tau_2' = \tau_2 - c_1\beta_1\tau_3. \tag{7.79}$$

The result is

$$\begin{vmatrix} U_1 & U_2 & 0 \\ -S_1V_1 - S_3V_2 & R_1V_1 + R_3V_2 & V_1 + P_1V_2 \\ (S_2 - S_1P_2)W_2 & (R_1P_2 - R_2)W_2 & W_1 + P_2W_2 \end{vmatrix} = 0. \tag{7.80}$$

This is independent of the arbitrary coefficients α_1, β_1, γ_1, c_1.

For practical nomography, only real values of P_1 and P_2 are of interest. Otherwise, a nomogram is impossible. We saw in Chapter II that Eq. (2.35) can be nomographed either as it stands or after cancellation of the common factor $q_2 - q_1$, and that the two nomograms obtained are not projective transforms of each other. We now find that the equation in Problem 7.7 can be nomographed as it stands but not after cancellation of the factor $\sin(u - v)$.

PROBLEM 7.9.   The proof is left as an exercise for the reader.

When several of the R's and S's vanish, degenerate cases may arise. For instance, in Eq. (2.22), let

$$\begin{aligned} U_1 &= u, & U_2 &= 1, \\ V_1 &= v, & V_2 &= 1, \\ W_1 &= w, & W_2 &= 1. \end{aligned} \right\} \tag{7.81}$$

Then, by Eq. (7.50) we see that

$$R_2 = 1, \quad S_3 = -1, \quad R_1 = R_3 = R_4 = S_1 = S_2 = S_4 = 0. \tag{7.82}$$

Hence from Eq. (7.61):

$$\gamma_1 c_2 = 0 \qquad (7.83)$$

and from Eq. (7.64):

$$\gamma_2 c_1 = 0. \qquad (7.84)$$

Since in Eqs. (7.69), (7.70), etc. c_1 and γ_1 appeared in the denominator, we must suppose nonzero values for them. Hence, from Eqs. (7.83) and (7.84):

$$c_2 = 0 \qquad (7.85)$$

and

$$\gamma_2 = 0 \qquad (7.86)$$

whence, from Eqs. (7.65) and (7.66):

$$P_1 = P_2 = 0. \qquad (7.87)$$

Hence, Eq. (7.80) becomes

$$\begin{vmatrix} u & +1 & 0 \\ +1 & 0 & v \\ 0 & -1 & w \end{vmatrix} = 0. \qquad (7.88)$$

Another degenerate case is given by Eq. (2.10). If Eqs. (7.81) are used, Eq. (7.61) leads to

$$c_1 \gamma_1 = 0. \qquad (7.89)$$

But then, either (7.69) or (7.70) becomes invalid. This difficulty is removed if we take

$$\begin{aligned} U_1 &= u, & U_2 &= 1, \\ V_1 &= 1, & V_2 &= v, \\ W_1 &= 1, & W_2 &= w. \end{aligned} \qquad (7.90)$$

PROBLEM 7.10. The details are left as an exercise for the reader.

Such degenerate cases are of little interest, since they can be solved easily by trial and error.

CHAPTER VIII

Nonprojective Transformations

8.1. Elementary Types

In Chapter II, we saw some isolated examples of nomograms capable of nonprojective transformations. For instance, Figs. 2.3, 2.4, and 3.9 (the latter with the a scale omitted) all give the product of two numbers. The question arises whether there exist other nomograms capable of nonprojective transformation. The answer was given by T.-H. Gronwall (see bibliography at the end of this book). His derivations require mathematics which is beyond the scope of this book; but the results are of practical value and will be given here, although the proofs must remain incomplete in some places. He proves the following theorem, which we must state without proof:

THEOREM 8.1. A nomogram is capable of nonprojective transformation if and only if it represents an equation of the form

$$f(u) + g(v) + h(w) = 0. \tag{8.1}$$

For instance, with $f(u) = u$, $g(v) = v$, and $h(w) = -w$, this gives Eq. (2.10). Or with $f(u) = \log u$, $g(v) = \log v$, and $h(w) = -\log w$, it becomes Eq. (2.20), which is equivalent to (2.21). Since such substitutions do not alter the basic problem of nomography, we shall only discuss the equation

$$u + v + w = 0 \tag{8.2}$$

with the understanding that three functions may be substituted for the respective variables.

113

Gronwall goes on to derive all possible nonprojectively related nomograms which represent Eq. (8.2), and he proves that there can be no others. The proof of the latter proposition must be omitted here. But we shall repeat Gronwall's enumeration of the possible nomograms and we shall prove in each case that the nomogram represents Eq. (8.2). Special cases of most of these nomograms were obtained previously by J. Clark.

The representations analogous to Figs. 2.2 and 2.4 will probably be obvious to the reader. The first is

$$\begin{vmatrix} u & 1 & 1 \\ v & 0 & 1 \\ -1/_2w & 1/_2 & 1 \end{vmatrix} = 0. \tag{8.3}$$

As for the second, we rewrite Eq. (8.2) in the form

$$e^{au}e^{av} = e^{-aw}, \tag{8.4}$$

which is analogous to Eq. (2.21). Its nomogram is described by the equation

$$\begin{vmatrix} e^{au} & 1 & 1 \\ 0 & \dfrac{1}{1 + e^{-av}} & 1 \\ -e^{-aw} & 0 & 1 \end{vmatrix} = 0 \tag{8.5}$$

analogous to Eq. (2.24). Here, a may be any real constant. A change in a constitutes a nonprojective transformation, whereas multiplication of u, v, and w in Eq. (8.3) would only constitute a stretch in the y direction.

PROBLEM 8.1. Prove that a change in the sign of a in Eq. (8.5) combined with a suitable projective transformation is equivalent to an interchange of u and v.

If the reader is acquainted with l'Hospital's rule, he may solve the following.

PROBLEM 8.2. Subject Eq. (8.5) to a projective transformation so that four selected scale points are projected to the coordinates shown in the following table:

$$\left.\begin{array}{lll} u = 0 & x = 1 & y = 0 \\ u = 1 & x = 1 & y = 1 \\ v = 0 & x = 0 & y = 0 \\ v = 1 & x = 0 & y = 1. \end{array}\right\} \quad (8.6)$$

Then, letting $a \to 0$, show that the nomogram tends to the form of Eq. (8.3) in the limit.

8.2. Generalized Circular Nomograms

Omitting the b scale from Fig. 3.9 and making obvious changes in notation, we obtain from Eq. (3.31):

$$\begin{vmatrix} \dfrac{1}{u^2 + 1} & \dfrac{u}{u^2 + 1} & 1 \\[2mm] \dfrac{1}{v^2 + 1} & \dfrac{v}{v^2 + 1} & 1 \\[2mm] 0 & -\dfrac{1}{w} & 1 \end{vmatrix} = 0. \quad (8.7)$$

We may modify Eq. (8.2) by writing it in the form

$$(u - u_0) + (v - v_0) + (w - w_0) = 0, \quad (8.8)$$

where u_0, v_0, w_0 are any three real constants which satisfy the relation

$$u_0 + v_0 + w_0 = 0. \quad (8.9)$$

In place of Eq. (8.7), we then obtain

$$\begin{vmatrix} \dfrac{1}{(u - u_0)^2 + 1} & \dfrac{u - u_0}{(u - u_0)^2 + 1} & 1 \\[3mm] \dfrac{1}{(v - v_0)^2 + 1} & \dfrac{v - v_0}{(v - v_0)^2 + 1} & 1 \\[3mm] 0 & -\dfrac{1}{w - w_0} & 1 \end{vmatrix} = 0. \quad (8.10)$$

By virtue of Eq. (8.9), only two of the three parameters in Eq. (8.10) are independent. Furthermore, any change in the parameters which leaves $u_0 - v_0$ unchanged is tantamount to a projective transformation.

PROBLEM 8.3. The proof is left as an exercise for the reader.

Barring projective transformations, we should regard Eq. (8.10) as the equation of a one-parameter family of nomograms.

PROBLEM 8.4. Prove that multiplication of u, v, and w in Eq. (8.7) by a common factor a is tantamount to a projective transformation.

Referring to Fig. 3.9, we see that, although the scale for q from $-\infty$ to $+\infty$ is contained in a finite portion of the plane, the portion of the scale corresponding to large absolute values of q is crowded and difficult to read. In the notation of Eq. (8.7), u and v have taken the place of q. The advantage of the generalization represented by Eq. (8.10) is that by a change of u_0 and v_0, we may move any portion of the u or v scale into that region where the graduation marks are widely separated, so that accurate readings are possible.

Equation (2.36) describes a nomogram which represents Eq. (2.33). Multiplying the first row through by $(q_1 - 1)/q_1$, the second by $(q_2 - 1)/q_2$, and the third by $1/\sqrt{b}$, we obtain

$$\begin{vmatrix} q_1 & 1 & 1 - \dfrac{1}{q_1} \\[2mm] q_2 & 1 & 1 - \dfrac{1}{q_2} \\[2mm] \sqrt{b} & 0 & \dfrac{1}{\sqrt{b}} \end{vmatrix} = 0. \tag{8.11}$$

Letting $q_1 = e^{2u}$, $q_2 = e^{2v}$, $b = e^{-2w}$, we obtain

$$\begin{vmatrix} e^{2u} & 1 & 1 - e^{-2u} \\ e^{2v} & 1 & 1 - e^{-2v} \\ e^{-w} & 0 & e^{w} \end{vmatrix} = 0 \tag{8.12}$$

as another representation of Eq. (8.2).   Transforming this by the matrix

$$[k] = \begin{bmatrix} 1 & 1 & 1 \\ -1 & 3 & -1 \\ 1 & -1 & -1 \end{bmatrix} \qquad (8.13)$$

(see Section 4.3), we obtain

$$\begin{vmatrix} e^{2u} - e^{-2u} & e^{2u} + 2 + e^{-2u} & e^{2u} - 2 + e^{-2u} \\ e^{2v} - e^{-2v} & e^{2v} + 2 + e^{-2v} & e^{2v} - 2 + e^{-2v} \\ e^{-w} + e^{w} & e^{-w} - e^{w} & e^{-w} - e^{w} \end{vmatrix} = 0 \qquad (8.14)$$

which may be written

$$\begin{vmatrix} (e^{u} - e^{-u})(e^{u} + e^{-u}) & (e^{u} + e^{-u})^2 & (e^{u} - e^{-u})^2 \\ (e^{v} - e^{-v})(e^{v} + e^{-v}) & (e^{v} + e^{-v})^2 & (e^{v} - e^{-v})^2 \\ e^{w} + e^{-w} & -(e^{w} - e^{-w}) & -(e^{w} - e^{-w}) \end{vmatrix} = 0. \qquad (8.15)$$

Dividing each row by its element in the last column and using the identity

$$\operatorname{ctnh} x = \frac{e^{x} + e^{-x}}{e^{x} - e^{-x}}, \qquad (8.16)$$

we obtain

$$\begin{vmatrix} \operatorname{ctnh} u & \operatorname{ctnh}^2 u & 1 \\ \operatorname{ctnh} v & \operatorname{ctnh}^2 v & 1 \\ -\operatorname{ctnh} w & 1 & 1 \end{vmatrix} = 0. \qquad (8.17)$$

This may be generalized to the form

$$\begin{vmatrix} \operatorname{ctnh} a(u - u_0) & \operatorname{ctnh}^2 a(u - u_0) & 1 \\ \operatorname{ctnh} a(v - v_0) & \operatorname{ctnh}^2 a(v - v_0) & 1 \\ -\operatorname{ctnh} a(w - w_0) & 1 & 1 \end{vmatrix} = 0 \qquad (8.18)$$

subject to Eq. (8.9).

Barring projective transformations, we may regard Eq. (8.18) as the equation of a two-parameter family of nomograms with a and $u_0 - v_0$ as parameters.

PROBLEM 8.5. Using the identities

$$\operatorname{ctnh} x = \frac{\cosh x}{\sinh x},$$

$$\sinh (x + y) = \sinh x \cosh y + \cosh x \sinh y,$$
$$\cosh (x + y) = \cosh x \cosh y + \sinh x \sinh y,$$

prove that a change in u_0, v_0, and w_0 in Eq. (8.18) such that $u_0 - v_0$ remains unchanged and Eq. (8.9) is still satisfied is tantamount to a projective transformation.

In general, only real values of the parameters a, u_0, v_0, w_0 are of interest, since only scale points with real coordinates x, y can be graphed in practice. An exceptional case occurs however when a is a pure imaginary. Let $a = ib$, where b is real. Making use of the identity

$$\operatorname{ctnh} ib = - i \operatorname{ctn} b$$

we obtain from Eq. (8.18) after dividing the first column by $-i$ and the second by -1:

$$\begin{vmatrix} \operatorname{ctn} b(u - u_0) & \operatorname{ctn}^2 b(u - u_0) & 1 \\ \operatorname{ctn} b(v - v_0) & \operatorname{ctn}^2 b(v - v_0) & 1 \\ -\operatorname{ctn} b(w - w_0) & -1 & 1 \end{vmatrix} = 0. \qquad (8.19)$$

This, like Eq. (8.18), represents a two-parameter family of nomograms. With $u_0 = v_0 = w_0 = 0$ and $b = 1$, this is the solution of Problem 7.7.

An interchange of u and w or of v and w in Eqs. (8.10), (8.18), and (8.19) is also tantamount to a nonprojective transformation but does not lead to any basically new types of nomograms.

PROBLEM 8.6. Solve Problem 5.4 using nonprojective as well as projective transformations.

8.3. Weierstrass' Elliptic Function

In a circular nomogram, two of the three scales coincide. The symmetrical form of Eq. (8.2) suggests that it should be possible to construct a nomogram for it where all three scales coincide. This is indeed the case. In order to show how this

can be done, we must introduce Weierstrass' elliptic function.
Let u be defined as a function of p by the equation

$$u = \int_p^\infty \frac{dx}{\sqrt{4x^3 - g_2 x - g_3}} \tag{8.20}$$

where g_2 and g_3 are parameters. The integral in Eq. (8.20)
belongs to the class of elliptic integrals. The inverse function
$p(u)$ is known as Weierstrass' elliptic function. Differentiating
both sides of Eq. (8.20) with respect to p, we obtain

$$\frac{du}{dp} = \frac{-1}{\sqrt{4p^3 - g_2 p - g_3}}. \tag{8.21}$$

Taking reciprocals of both sides and squaring, we obtain a
differential equation satisfied by $p(u)$:

$$\left(\frac{dp}{du}\right)^2 = 4p^3 - g_2 p - g_3. \tag{8.22}$$

Let us write

$$y = -\frac{dp}{du} \tag{8.23}$$

and

$$x = p \tag{8.24}$$

and plot y against x.   Figure 8.1 shows an example of such a plot
with $g_2 = +1200$ and $g_3 = -12000$. Here, the cubic equation

$$4x^3 - g_2 x - g_3 = 0 \tag{8.25}$$

has only one real root. Figure 8.3 shows another example with
$g_2 = +1200$ and $g_3 = -4000$. Here, Eq. (8.25) has three
real roots.

To evaluate u as a function of p, we use Eq. (8.20). When
p is large, we may use the approximation

$$u = \int_p^\infty \frac{dx}{\sqrt{4x^3}} = \frac{1}{\sqrt{p}}. \tag{8.26}$$

Starting with a value of p large enough so that Eq. (8.26) gives the desired degree of accuracy, we evaluate u for smaller values of p by Simpson's rule. For those ranges of values of x where the integrand in Eq. (8.20) is small, a large tabular difference will give sufficient accuracy. Where the integrand is large, a smaller tabular difference must be used. As x approaches the largest real root of Eq. (8.25), the integrand tends to infinity, so that Simpson's rule cannot be used. In the immediate vicinity of this root, we may use a linear approximation to the quantity under the square root sign in Eq. (8.20). We may determine two constants k and l such that, in the immediate vicinity of the largest real root of Eq. (8.25), we have the approximation

$$4x^3 - g_2 x - g_3 \simeq kx + l. \tag{8.27}$$

In this region, we can evaluate the indefinite integral

$$\int \frac{dx}{\sqrt{4x^3 - g_2 x - g_3}} \simeq \int \frac{dx}{\sqrt{kx + l}} = \frac{2}{k} \sqrt{kx + l}. \tag{8.28}$$

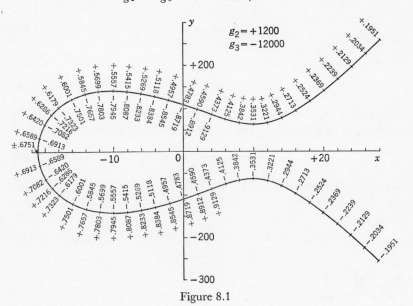

Figure 8.1

This is used to bridge the gap between the root in question and the point where the Simpson's rule integration was broken off. The integration may be continued beyond this root, but we shall postpone this matter for the moment.   If the largest real root of Eq. (8.25) is multiple, the approximation of Eq. (8.27) breaks down.   This case will also be postponed for the time being.

Values of u determined as described are marked on the curve in Fig. 8.1.   The square root in Eqs. (8.20) and (8.21) may be positive or negative.   We have adopted the convention that u is positive, starting from zero at $x = \infty$, when y is positive, and that u is negative, subject to the same initial condition, when y is negative.   The curve marked with values of u forms a scale, and we shall prove that this scale forms a nomogram which represents Eq. (8.2) and where the scales for u, v, and w coincide.   This type of nomogram was invented by T.-H. Gronwall, but the relevant property of the function $p(u)$ was discovered by K. Weierstrass.   The elementary proof which we shall give is due to N. H. Abel.

8.4. Abel's Proof

From Eqs. (8.22), (8.23), and (8.24), we have

$$y^2 = 4x^3 - g_2 x - g_3, \tag{8.29}$$

the equation of the curve in Fig. 8.1.   From Eqs. (8.23) and (8.24), we have

$$du = -\frac{dx}{y}. \tag{8.30}$$

The straight line

$$y = mx + n \tag{8.31}$$

characterized by the parameters m and n may be so positioned that it intersects the curve of Eq. (8.29) in three (real) points for which x takes on the values x_1, x_2, and x_3.   Eliminating y between Eqs. (8.29) and (8.31), we obtain

$$4x^3 - g_2x - g_3 - (mx + n)^2 = 0. \tag{8.32}$$

The left-hand member of this equation will be denoted by $\varphi(x)$. It may be factored as follows:

$$\varphi(x) = 4(x - x_1)(x - x_2)(x - x_3). \tag{8.33}$$

We shall rule out the case where two or more of the roots of $\varphi(x)$ coincide.

Equation (8.32) is satisfied by three values of x, to which we shall refer collectively as x_r, with $r = 1, 2,$ or 3. These should not be confused with the roots of Eq. (8.25). Any x_r may be regarded as a function of the parameters m and n of the straight line. Let x_r, m, and n change by infinitesimal increments in such a manner that $\varphi(x_r)$ remains equal to zero. Then

$$\varphi'(x_r)\delta x_r + \frac{\partial \varphi}{\partial m}\, \delta m + \frac{\partial \varphi}{\partial n}\, \delta n = 0, \tag{8.34}$$

where we have written $\varphi'(x_r)$ for the value of $\partial \varphi/\partial x$ when $x = x_r$. The other two partial derivatives of φ are easily evaluated from the definition of this function:

$$\frac{\partial \varphi}{\partial m} = -2x_r(mx_r + n) \tag{8.35}$$

$$\frac{\partial \varphi}{\partial n} = -2(mx_r + n). \tag{8.36}$$

Substituting into Eq. (8.34) and rearranging, we obtain

$$\frac{\delta x_r}{mx_r + n} = \frac{2(x_r\delta m + \delta n)}{\varphi'(x_r)}. \tag{8.37}$$

The denominator of the left-hand member of this equation gives the value of y in Eq. (8.29) corresponding to x_r, since the scale and the straight line intersect at this point. Referring to Eq. (8.30), we see that the left-hand member of Eq. (8.37) equals $-\delta u$. Now let us write Eq. (8.37) for the three values of r and add up the resulting equations. Distinguishing by u, v, and w the three values of u corresponding respectively to $x = x_1$, x_2, and x_3, we obtain

$$-\delta u - \delta v - \delta w = 2\left[\frac{x_1\delta m + \delta n}{\varphi'(x_1)} + \frac{x_2\delta m + \delta n}{\varphi'(x_2)} + \frac{x_3\delta m + \delta n}{\varphi'(x_3)}\right]. \quad (8.38)$$

Consider now the function

$$\delta\psi(x) = \frac{x(x\delta m + \delta n)}{\varphi(x)}, \quad (8.39)$$

which has the property that

$$\delta\psi(0) = 0 \quad (8.40)$$

provided that none of the x_r's equals zero.   Using Eq. (8.33), we expand $\delta\psi(x)$ in partial fractions:

$$\delta\psi(x) = \frac{A_1}{x - x_1} + \frac{A_2}{x - x_2} + \frac{A_3}{x - x_3}. \quad (8.41)$$

The numerators are evaluated by the rule

$$A_r = \lim_{x \to x_r} (x - x_r)\delta\psi(x). \quad (8.42)$$

With the aid of l'Hospital's rule, this gives

$$A_r = \frac{x_r(x_r\delta m + \delta n)}{\varphi'(x_r)}. \quad (8.43)$$

Substituting into Eq. (8.41), we obtain

$$\delta\psi(x) = \frac{x_1(x_1\delta m + \delta n)}{(x - x_1)\varphi'(x_1)} + \frac{x_2(x_2\delta m + \delta n)}{(x - x_2)\varphi'(x_2)} + \frac{x_3(x_3\delta m + \delta n)}{(x - x_3)\varphi'(x_3)}. \quad (8.44)$$

Setting $x = 0$ and using Eq. (8.40), we obtain

$$-\frac{x_1\delta m + \delta n}{\varphi'(x_1)} - \frac{x_2\delta m + \delta n}{\varphi'(x_2)} - \frac{x_3\delta m + \delta n}{\varphi'(x_3)} = 0. \quad (8.45)$$

From this and Eq. (8.38), we obtain

$$\delta u + \delta v + \delta w = 0, \quad (8.46)$$

whence, by integration

$$u + v + w = \text{constant.} \quad (8.47)$$

This constant remains to be evaluated.   Although, for

the purpose of the proof, we ruled out the possibility that the line may be tangent to the scale (two equal roots of $\varphi(x)$), this case may be approached as a limit. In particular, if the line is tangent to the curve at a point of inflection, we have the limiting case $u = v = w$, so that the constant in Eq. (8.47) is three times the value of u at a point of inflection. Subjecting Fig. 8.1 to the projective transformation

$$x' = \frac{x}{y},\qquad (8.48)$$

$$y' = \frac{1}{y},\qquad (8.49)$$

we obtain Fig. 8.2. The point at infinity of the curve in Fig. 8.1, where the initial conditions in Eq. (8.20) were given, thus transforms into the origin of Fig. 8.2 and turns out to be a point of inflection. There, $u = 0$. Hence, Eq. (8.47) becomes Eq. (8.2) and the proposition is proved.

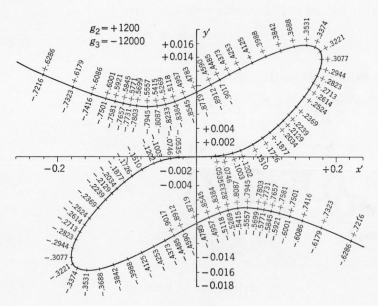

Figure 8.2

8.5. Discussion

Unfortunately, the scale in Fig. 8.2 has two other points of inflection, namely at $u = \pm 0.4501$. Hence, the constant in Eq. (8.47) is multiple-valued. Indeed, we shall show that $p(u)$ is a periodic function. Referring again to Fig. 8.1, we start out with a straight line which intersects the scale in two points with $y > 0$ and one point with $y < 0$, for instance $u = +0.2524$, $v = +0.3842$, $w = -0.6366$, we hold v constant and let u approach v continuously. Soon the point of intersection corresponding to w passes the apex of the curve (the minimum of x) and proceeds to a portion of the curve where $y > 0$. If the constant in Eq. (8.47) is to remain zero, we must suppose that u is continuous at the apex of the curve. The evaluation of u beyond the apex proceeds along the same lines as before, except that $|u|$ now increases with increasing x. However, a short cut is now possible, since the change in u between any two values of x (for a given sign of y) does not depend on the starting value of u. For instance, in Fig. 8.1, for $y > 0$, at $x = -14$, we have $u = +0.5845$, and at $x = -4$, we have $u = +0.5118$. The difference between these two values of u is 0.0727. Alternatively, at $x = -14$, we could have $u = -0.7657$, and at $x = -4$, we would then have $u = -0.8384$. Here, also, the difference between the two values of u is 0.0727. This follows from the fact that the value of the integrand in Eq. (8.20) depends only on x and not on the value of u already attained. Thanks to this short cut, the numerical integration from $x = \infty$ to the apex of the curve need be carried out only once.

We may regard the curve in Fig. 8.1 as a closed curve which always has one point at infinity, no matter how it is transformed by projection. We may continue the evaluation of u beyond this point, just as we continued it beyond the apex of the curve. Thus, we may extend the u scale indefinitely, tracing out the curve repeatedly. Since the same constant increment is added to u each time the curve is retraced from any given starting point, it will be seen that $p(u)$ is a periodic function of u. A more thorough investigation of this interesting property of Weierstrass' function would require the use of complex values of u and $p(u)$ and is beyond the scope of this book.

If Eq. (8.25) has three real roots, the scale will have two branches, which we shall call A and B, where A corresponds to smaller values of x. This case is illustrated in Fig. 8.3, where

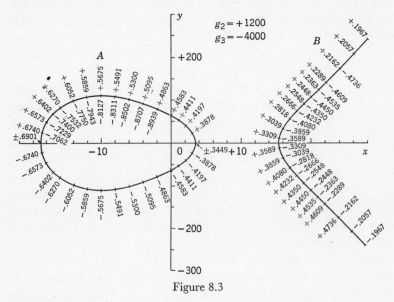

Figure 8.3

we have taken $g_2 = +1200$ and $g_3 = -4000$. The branch B alone forms a complete nomogram. However, because of the low curvature of the portion of branch B shown (except in the vicinity of the apex), its use is impractical unless it is strongly contracted in the direction of its tangent at one of its points of inflection, which are located at $u = \pm 0.2300$.

In the gap between the two branches, the integrand in Eq. (8.20) becomes imaginary and may have two possible signs, as before. On branch A, the integrand is real once again. Here, u is complex, but its imaginary part is constant all over branch A. The two possible values of the imaginary part have opposite signs but the same absolute value. If a straight line intersects branch A in two points, it will intersect branch B in one point. Let the two scale values on A be denoted by u and v, and that on B by w. Then u and v must have imaginary parts which are equal in absolute value and opposite in sign; and since w is real, the imaginary part of $u + v + w$ will vanish, as it should. The real part of $u + v + w$ will also vanish. Only the real part has been indicated on branch A in Fig. 8.3.

Variants of this type of nomogram can be obtained by replacing u, v, and w respectively with $u - u_0$, $v - v_0$, and $w - w_0$, where u_0, v_0, and w_0 are parameters subject to Eq. (8.9). Thus, we have four independent parameters u_0, v_0, g_2, and g_3, a change in any one or more of which constitutes a nonprojective transformation. But multiplication of $u - u_0$, $v - v_0$, and $w - w_0$ by a constant factor does not constitute a new kind of transformation. For if we multiply x in Eqs. (8.20) and (8.29) by a constant factor, we achieve a change in the scale variable u combined with a stretch in the x direction. But the same effect could have been obtained by suitable changes in g_2 and g_3 and a stretch in the y direction.

PROBLEM 8.7. The proof is left as an exercise for the reader.

8.6. Degenerate Cases

A degenerate case occurs if two or more of the roots of Eq. (8.25) coincide. Let the left-hand member of Eq. (8.25) be denoted by $X(x)$. We locate the extremes (maximum and minimum) of this function by equating its first derivative to zero:

$$\frac{dX}{dx} = 12x^2 - g_2 = 0 \tag{8.50}$$

if

$$x = \pm\sqrt{\frac{g_2}{12}}. \tag{8.51}$$

These can be real only if $g_2 \geq 0$. If one of the values of x given by Eq. (8.51) satisfies Eq. (8.25), the latter has a double root. In this case, $p(u)$ becomes an elementary function. Consider first the case where the double root is positive. Substituting from Eq. (8.51) into Eq. (8.25) and solving for g_3, we obtain

$$g_3 = - \left(\frac{g_2}{3}\right)^{3/2}. \tag{8.52}$$

Now let g_2 be expressed in terms of another parameter a:

$$g_2 = \frac{4}{3} a^4. \tag{8.53}$$

Then, by Eq. (8.52):

$$g_3 = - \frac{8}{27} a^6. \tag{8.54}$$

The integral in Eq. (8.20) may now be evaluated by elementary methods, and the resulting equation may be solved for p, yielding

$$p(u) = \frac{a^2}{\sinh^2 au} + \frac{a^2}{3}. \tag{8.55}$$

PROBLEM 8.8. As an exercise the reader may verify by substitution that this solution satisfies the differential equation (8.22) and the boundary condition in Eq. (8.20), that is $p \rightarrow \infty$ as $u \rightarrow 0$.

Here, as in the preceding section, the nomogram is described by the equation

$$\begin{vmatrix} -\dfrac{dp(u)}{du} & p(u) & 1 \\[2mm] -\dfrac{dp(v)}{dv} & p(v) & 1 \\[2mm] -\dfrac{dp(w)}{dw} & p(w) & 1 \end{vmatrix} = 0. \tag{8.56}$$

PROBLEM 8.9. As an exercise the reader should plot the nomogram given by Eq. (8.56) with $g_2 = +1200$, that is $a^2 =$

30 and $g_3 = -8000$. Its form will be intermediate between Figs. 8.1 and 8.3. The two branches of Fig. 8.3 now have one point in common. Again, branch B alone is a complete nomogram in itself. Again, u is complex on branch A.

In Eq. (8.55), u, v, and w may be replaced respectively with $u - u_0$, $v - v_0$, and $w - w_0$, with u_0, v_0, and w_0 subject to Eq. (8.9). Apart from projective transformations, we now have three independent parameters a, u_0, v_0.

In the other degenerate case, the square root in Eq. (8.51) is negative, and the double root of Eq. (8.25) is negative. We retain Eq. (8.53) as a definition of a and replace Eq. (8.54) with

$$g_3 = + \frac{8}{27} a^6 \qquad (8.57)$$

and Eq. (8.55) with

$$p(u) = \frac{a^2}{\sin^2 au} - \frac{a^2}{3}. \qquad (8.58)$$

This case is closely analogous to the preceding.

PROBLEM 8.10. The details are left as an exercise for the reader and the problems analogous to Problems 8.8 and 8.9 should be solved.

Branch A of Fig. 8.3 has now shrunk to a point, which is located at $x = -10$, $y = 0$ when $g_2 = +1200$.

A doubly degenerate case occurs if $g_2 = g_3 = 0$, so that Eq. (8.25) has three coincident roots. In this case, Eq. (8.26) becomes exact, so that

$$p(u) = 1/u^2. \qquad (8.59)$$

This is substituted into Eq. (8.56) as before. Again, u, v, and w may be replaced respectively with $u - u_0$, $v - v_0$, and $w - w_0$ subject to Eq. (8.9). Apart from projective transformations, there are now two independent parameters u_0 and v_0. It is easily seen that multiplication of $u - u_0$, $v - v_0$, and $w - w_0$ by a constant factor is tantamount to unequal stretches in the x and y directions.

BIBLIOGRAPHY

The following is a list of publications that the reader may find useful for further study. No attempt has been made at comprehensiveness.

[1] Adams, D. P., "Alignment Diagrams from Network Charts by Graphics." *Mech. Eng.*, **78,** 1013 (1956).

[2] Allcock, H. J., and Jones, J. R., *The Nomogram*, 4th Ed., Sir Isaac Pitman and Sons, London, 1950.

[3] Clark, J., "Théorie génerale des abaques d'alignement de tout ordre." *Rev. mécanique*, **21,** 321–335, 576–585 (1907).

[4] Ford, L. R., *Notre Dame Mathematical Lectures*, **no. 4,** 1944.

[5] Gronwall, T.-H., Sur les équations à trois variables représentables par des nomogrammes à point alignés. *J. math. pures et appl. (Liouville)*, Ser. 6, **8,** 59–102 (1912).

[6] Kellogg, O. D., "Nomograms with Points in Alignment." *Z. Math. Phys.*, **63,** 159 (1915).

[7] Lafay, A., "Note sur la représentation approchée des équations à trois variables." *Le Génie Civil*, **40,** 289 (1902).

[8] Lambert, René, *Structure Générale des Nomogrammes et Systèms Nomographiques*, Hermann & Cie., Paris, 1937. Deals with generalizations of a nomogram where transparencies bearing grids may take the place of the straight-line index.

[9] d'Ocagne, M., *Traité de Nomographie*, Gautier-Villars, Paris, 1889. This book by the inventor of nomograms still has not lost its usefulness.

[10] Schmeidler, W., *Determinanten und Matrizen*, Akademie-Verlag, Berlin, 1949.

[11] Whittaker, E. T. and Watson, G. N., "Elliptic Functions. General Theorems and the Weierstrassian Function." *Modern Analysis*, Cambridge University Press, 1927, Chap. XX.

INDEX